# NEW YORK NOTARY LOG BOOK

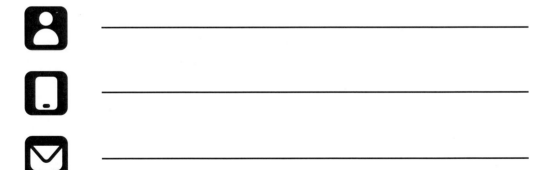

# NOTARY RECORD

| Printed Name and Address of Signer: | Phone number: | Thumb Print: |
|---|---|---|
| | Email: | |
| | Signer's Signature: | |

| Service Performed | Identification | | ID Number: | |
|---|---|---|---|---|
| ☐ Jurat | ☐ ID Card | ☐ Credible Witness | Issued By: | |
| ☐ Oath | ☐ Passport | ☐ Known Personally | | |
| ☐ Acknowledgement | ☐ Drivers License | | Date Issued: | Expiration Date: |
| ☐ Other _____ | ☐ Other _____ | | | |

| Document Type | Date/Time Notarized: | Document Date: | Fee Charged: |
|---|---|---|---|

| Printed Name and Address of Witness: | Phone number: |
|---|---|
| | Email: |
| | Signer's Signature: |

| Comments | Record Number |
|---|---|

# NOTARY RECORD

| Printed Name and Address of Signer: | Phone number: | Thumb Print: |
|---|---|---|
| | Email: | |
| | Signer's Signature: | |

| Service Performed | Identification | | ID Number: | |
|---|---|---|---|---|
| ☐ Jurat | ☐ ID Card | ☐ Credible Witness | Issued By: | |
| ☐ Oath | ☐ Passport | ☐ Known Personally | | |
| ☐ Acknowledgement | ☐ Drivers License | | Date Issued: | Expiration Date: |
| ☐ Other _____ | ☐ Other _____ | | | |

| Document Type | Date/Time Notarized: | Document Date: | Fee Charged: |
|---|---|---|---|

| Printed Name and Address of Witness: | Phone number: |
|---|---|
| | Email: |
| | Signer's Signature: |

| Comments | Record Number |
|---|---|

# NOTARY RECORD

| Printed Name and Address of Signer: | Phone number: | Thumb Print: |
|---|---|---|
| | Email: | |
| | Signer's Signature: | |

| **Service Performed** | **Identification** | ID Number: | |
|---|---|---|---|
| ☐ Jurat | ☐ ID Card   ☐ Credible Witness | Issued By: | |
| ☐ Oath | ☐ Passport   ☐ Known Personally | | |
| ☐ Acknowledgement | ☐ Drivers License | Date Issued: | Expiration Date: |
| ☐ Other _____ | ☐ Other _____ | | |

| Document Type | Date/Time Notarized: | Document Date: | Fee Charged: |
|---|---|---|---|

| Printed Name and Address of Witness: | Phone number: |
|---|---|
| | Email: |
| | Signer's Signature: |

| Comments | Record Number |
|---|---|

# NOTARY RECORD

| Printed Name and Address of Signer: | Phone number: | Thumb Print: |
|---|---|---|
| | Email: | |
| | Signer's Signature: | |

| **Service Performed** | **Identification** | ID Number: | |
|---|---|---|---|
| ☐ Jurat | ☐ ID Card   ☐ Credible Witness | Issued By: | |
| ☐ Oath | ☐ Passport   ☐ Known Personally | | |
| ☐ Acknowledgement | ☐ Drivers License | Date Issued: | Expiration Date: |
| ☐ Other _____ | ☐ Other _____ | | |

| Document Type | Date/Time Notarized: | Document Date: | Fee Charged: |
|---|---|---|---|

| Printed Name and Address of Witness: | Phone number: |
|---|---|
| | Email: |
| | Signer's Signature: |

| Comments | Record Number |
|---|---|

# NOTARY RECORD

| Printed Name and Address of Signer: | Phone number: | Thumb Print: |
|---|---|---|
| | Email: | |
| | Signer's Signature: | |

| Service Performed | Identification | ID Number: | |
|---|---|---|---|
| ☐ Jurat | ☐ ID Card    ☐ Credible Witness | Issued By: | |
| ☐ Oath | ☐ Passport    ☐ Known Personally | | |
| ☐ Acknowledgement | ☐ Drivers License | Date Issued: | Expiration Date: |
| ☐ Other _____ | ☐ Other _____ | | |

| Document Type | Date/Time Notarized: | Document Date: | Fee Charged: |
|---|---|---|---|

| Printed Name and Address of Witness: | Phone number: |
|---|---|
| | Email: |
| | Signer's Signature: |

| Comments | Record Number |
|---|---|

# NOTARY RECORD

| Printed Name and Address of Signer: | Phone number: | Thumb Print: |
|---|---|---|
| | Email: | |
| | Signer's Signature: | |

| Service Performed | Identification | ID Number: | |
|---|---|---|---|
| ☐ Jurat | ☐ ID Card    ☐ Credible Witness | Issued By: | |
| ☐ Oath | ☐ Passport    ☐ Known Personally | | |
| ☐ Acknowledgement | ☐ Drivers License | Date Issued: | Expiration Date: |
| ☐ Other _____ | ☐ Other _____ | | |

| Document Type | Date/Time Notarized: | Document Date: | Fee Charged: |
|---|---|---|---|

| Printed Name and Address of Witness: | Phone number: |
|---|---|
| | Email: |
| | Signer's Signature: |

| Comments | Record Number |
|---|---|

# NOTARY RECORD

| Printed Name and Address of Signer: | Phone number: | Thumb Print: |
|---|---|---|
| | Email: | |
| | Signer's Signature: | |

| **Service Performed** | **Identification** | | ID Number: | |
|---|---|---|---|---|
| ☐ Jurat | ☐ ID Card | ☐ Credible Witness | Issued By: | |
| ☐ Oath | ☐ Passport | ☐ Known Personally | | |
| ☐ Acknowledgement | ☐ Drivers License | | Date Issued: | Expiration Date: |
| ☐ Other _____ | ☐ Other _____ | | | |

| Document Type | Date/Time Notarized: | Document Date: | Fee Charged: |
|---|---|---|---|

| Printed Name and Address of Witness: | Phone number: |
|---|---|
| | Email: |
| | Signer's Signature: |

| Comments | Record Number |
|---|---|

# NOTARY RECORD

| Printed Name and Address of Signer: | Phone number: | Thumb Print: |
|---|---|---|
| | Email: | |
| | Signer's Signature: | |

| **Service Performed** | **Identification** | | ID Number: | |
|---|---|---|---|---|
| ☐ Jurat | ☐ ID Card | ☐ Credible Witness | Issued By: | |
| ☐ Oath | ☐ Passport | ☐ Known Personally | | |
| ☐ Acknowledgement | ☐ Drivers License | | Date Issued: | Expiration Date: |
| ☐ Other _____ | ☐ Other _____ | | | |

| Document Type | Date/Time Notarized: | Document Date: | Fee Charged: |
|---|---|---|---|

| Printed Name and Address of Witness: | Phone number: |
|---|---|
| | Email: |
| | Signer's Signature: |

| Comments | Record Number |
|---|---|

# NOTARY RECORD

| Printed Name and Address of Signer: | Phone number: | Thumb Print: |
|---|---|---|
| | Email: | |
| | Signer's Signature: | |

| Service Performed | Identification | | ID Number: | |
|---|---|---|---|---|
| ☐ Jurat | ☐ ID Card | ☐ Credible Witness | Issued By: | |
| ☐ Oath | ☐ Passport | ☐ Known Personally | | |
| ☐ Acknowledgement | ☐ Drivers License | | Date Issued: | Expiration Date: |
| ☐ Other _____ | ☐ Other _____ | | | |

| Document Type | Date/Time Notarized: | Document Date: | Fee Charged: |
|---|---|---|---|

| Printed Name and Address of Witness: | Phone number: |
|---|---|
| | Email: |
| | Signer's Signature: |

| Comments | Record Number |
|---|---|

---

# NOTARY RECORD

| Printed Name and Address of Signer: | Phone number: | Thumb Print: |
|---|---|---|
| | Email: | |
| | Signer's Signature: | |

| Service Performed | Identification | | ID Number: | |
|---|---|---|---|---|
| ☐ Jurat | ☐ ID Card | ☐ Credible Witness | Issued By: | |
| ☐ Oath | ☐ Passport | ☐ Known Personally | | |
| ☐ Acknowledgement | ☐ Drivers License | | Date Issued: | Expiration Date: |
| ☐ Other _____ | ☐ Other _____ | | | |

| Document Type | Date/Time Notarized: | Document Date: | Fee Charged: |
|---|---|---|---|

| Printed Name and Address of Witness: | Phone number: |
|---|---|
| | Email: |
| | Signer's Signature: |

| Comments | Record Number |
|---|---|

# NOTARY RECORD

| Printed Name and Address of Signer: | Phone number: | Thumb Print: |
|---|---|---|
| | Email: | |
| | Signer's Signature: | |

| Service Performed | Identification | | ID Number: | |
|---|---|---|---|---|
| ☐ Jurat | ☐ ID Card | ☐ Credible Witness | | |
| ☐ Oath | ☐ Passport | ☐ Known Personally | Issued By: | |
| ☐ Acknowledgement | ☐ Drivers License | | | |
| ☐ Other _____ | ☐ Other _____ | | Date Issued: | Expiration Date: |

| Document Type | Date/Time Notarized: | Document Date: | Fee Charged: |
|---|---|---|---|

| Printed Name and Address of Witness: | Phone number: |
|---|---|
| | Email: |
| | Signer's Signature: |

| Comments | Record Number |
|---|---|

# NOTARY RECORD

| Printed Name and Address of Signer: | Phone number: | Thumb Print: |
|---|---|---|
| | Email: | |
| | Signer's Signature: | |

| Service Performed | Identification | | ID Number: | |
|---|---|---|---|---|
| ☐ Jurat | ☐ ID Card | ☐ Credible Witness | | |
| ☐ Oath | ☐ Passport | ☐ Known Personally | Issued By: | |
| ☐ Acknowledgement | ☐ Drivers License | | | |
| ☐ Other _____ | ☐ Other _____ | | Date Issued: | Expiration Date: |

| Document Type | Date/Time Notarized: | Document Date: | Fee Charged: |
|---|---|---|---|

| Printed Name and Address of Witness: | Phone number: |
|---|---|
| | Email: |
| | Signer's Signature: |

| Comments | Record Number |
|---|---|

# NOTARY RECORD

| Printed Name and Address of Signer: | Phone number: | Thumb Print: |
|---|---|---|
| | Email: | |
| | Signer's Signature: | |

| Service Performed | Identification | | ID Number: | |
|---|---|---|---|---|
| ☐ Jurat | ☐ ID Card | ☐ Credible Witness | Issued By: | |
| ☐ Oath | ☐ Passport | ☐ Known Personally | | |
| ☐ Acknowledgement | ☐ Drivers License | | Date Issued: | Expiration Date: |
| ☐ Other _____ | ☐ Other _____ | | | |

| Document Type | Date/Time Notarized: | Document Date: | Fee Charged: |
|---|---|---|---|

| Printed Name and Address of Witness: | Phone number: |
|---|---|
| | Email: |
| | Signer's Signature: |

| Comments | Record Number |
|---|---|

---

# NOTARY RECORD

| Printed Name and Address of Signer: | Phone number: | Thumb Print: |
|---|---|---|
| | Email: | |
| | Signer's Signature: | |

| Service Performed | Identification | | ID Number: | |
|---|---|---|---|---|
| ☐ Jurat | ☐ ID Card | ☐ Credible Witness | Issued By: | |
| ☐ Oath | ☐ Passport | ☐ Known Personally | | |
| ☐ Acknowledgement | ☐ Drivers License | | Date Issued: | Expiration Date: |
| ☐ Other _____ | ☐ Other _____ | | | |

| Document Type | Date/Time Notarized: | Document Date: | Fee Charged: |
|---|---|---|---|

| Printed Name and Address of Witness: | Phone number: |
|---|---|
| | Email: |
| | Signer's Signature: |

| Comments | Record Number |
|---|---|

# NOTARY RECORD

| Printed Name and Address of Signer: | Phone number: | Thumb Print: |
|---|---|---|
| | Email: | |
| | Signer's Signature: | |

| Service Performed | Identification | ID Number: | |
|---|---|---|---|
| ☐ Jurat | ☐ ID Card   ☐ Credible Witness | Issued By: | |
| ☐ Oath | ☐ Passport   ☐ Known Personally | | |
| ☐ Acknowledgement | ☐ Drivers License | Date Issued: | Expiration Date: |
| ☐ Other _____ | ☐ Other _____ | | |

| Document Type | Date/Time Notarized: | Document Date: | Fee Charged: |
|---|---|---|---|

| Printed Name and Address of Witness: | Phone number: |
|---|---|
| | Email: |
| | Signer's Signature: |

| Comments | Record Number |
|---|---|

---

# NOTARY RECORD

| Printed Name and Address of Signer: | Phone number: | Thumb Print: |
|---|---|---|
| | Email: | |
| | Signer's Signature: | |

| Service Performed | Identification | ID Number: | |
|---|---|---|---|
| ☐ Jurat | ☐ ID Card   ☐ Credible Witness | Issued By: | |
| ☐ Oath | ☐ Passport   ☐ Known Personally | | |
| ☐ Acknowledgement | ☐ Drivers License | Date Issued: | Expiration Date: |
| ☐ Other _____ | ☐ Other _____ | | |

| Document Type | Date/Time Notarized: | Document Date: | Fee Charged: |
|---|---|---|---|

| Printed Name and Address of Witness: | Phone number: |
|---|---|
| | Email: |
| | Signer's Signature: |

| Comments | Record Number |
|---|---|

# NOTARY RECORD

| Printed Name and Address of Signer: | Phone number: | Thumb Print: |
|---|---|---|
| | Email: | |
| | Signer's Signature: | |

| **Service Performed** | **Identification** | ID Number: | |
|---|---|---|---|
| ☐ Jurat | ☐ ID Card  ☐ Credible Witness | Issued By: | |
| ☐ Oath | ☐ Passport  ☐ Known Personally | | |
| ☐ Acknowledgement | ☐ Drivers License | Date Issued: | Expiration Date: |
| ☐ Other _____ | ☐ Other _____ | | |

| Document Type | Date/Time Notarized: | Document Date: | Fee Charged: |
|---|---|---|---|

| Printed Name and Address of Witness: | Phone number: |
|---|---|
| | Email: |
| | Signer's Signature: |

| Comments | Record Number |
|---|---|

# NOTARY RECORD

| Printed Name and Address of Signer: | Phone number: | Thumb Print: |
|---|---|---|
| | Email: | |
| | Signer's Signature: | |

| **Service Performed** | **Identification** | ID Number: | |
|---|---|---|---|
| ☐ Jurat | ☐ ID Card  ☐ Credible Witness | Issued By: | |
| ☐ Oath | ☐ Passport  ☐ Known Personally | | |
| ☐ Acknowledgement | ☐ Drivers License | Date Issued: | Expiration Date: |
| ☐ Other _____ | ☐ Other _____ | | |

| Document Type | Date/Time Notarized: | Document Date: | Fee Charged: |
|---|---|---|---|

| Printed Name and Address of Witness: | Phone number: |
|---|---|
| | Email: |
| | Signer's Signature: |

| Comments | Record Number |
|---|---|

# NOTARY RECORD

| Printed Name and Address of Signer: | Phone number: | Thumb Print: |
|---|---|---|
| | Email: | |
| | Signer's Signature: | |

| Service Performed | Identification | ID Number: | |
|---|---|---|---|
| ☐ Jurat | ☐ ID Card  ☐ Credible Witness | Issued By: | |
| ☐ Oath | ☐ Passport  ☐ Known Personally | | |
| ☐ Acknowledgement | ☐ Drivers License | Date Issued: | Expiration Date: |
| ☐ Other _____ | ☐ Other _____ | | |

| Document Type | Date/Time Notarized: | Document Date: | Fee Charged: |
|---|---|---|---|

| Printed Name and Address of Witness: | Phone number: |
|---|---|
| | Email: |
| | Signer's Signature: |

| Comments | Record Number |
|---|---|

# NOTARY RECORD

| Printed Name and Address of Signer: | Phone number: | Thumb Print: |
|---|---|---|
| | Email: | |
| | Signer's Signature: | |

| Service Performed | Identification | ID Number: | |
|---|---|---|---|
| ☐ Jurat | ☐ ID Card  ☐ Credible Witness | Issued By: | |
| ☐ Oath | ☐ Passport  ☐ Known Personally | | |
| ☐ Acknowledgement | ☐ Drivers License | Date Issued: | Expiration Date: |
| ☐ Other _____ | ☐ Other _____ | | |

| Document Type | Date/Time Notarized: | Document Date: | Fee Charged: |
|---|---|---|---|

| Printed Name and Address of Witness: | Phone number: |
|---|---|
| | Email: |
| | Signer's Signature: |

| Comments | Record Number |
|---|---|

# NOTARY RECORD

| Printed Name and Address of Signer: | Phone number: | Thumb Print: |
|---|---|---|
| | Email: | |
| | Signer's Signature: | |

| Service Performed | Identification | | ID Number: | |
|---|---|---|---|---|
| ☐ Jurat | ☐ ID Card | ☐ Credible Witness | Issued By: | |
| ☐ Oath | ☐ Passport | ☐ Known Personally | | |
| ☐ Acknowledgement | ☐ Drivers License | | Date Issued: | Expiration Date: |
| ☐ Other _____ | ☐ Other _____ | | | |

| Document Type | Date/Time Notarized: | Document Date: | Fee Charged: |
|---|---|---|---|

| Printed Name and Address of Witness: | Phone number: |
|---|---|
| | Email: |
| | Signer's Signature: |

| Comments | Record Number |
|---|---|

# NOTARY RECORD

| Printed Name and Address of Signer: | Phone number: | Thumb Print: |
|---|---|---|
| | Email: | |
| | Signer's Signature: | |

| Service Performed | Identification | | ID Number: | |
|---|---|---|---|---|
| ☐ Jurat | ☐ ID Card | ☐ Credible Witness | Issued By: | |
| ☐ Oath | ☐ Passport | ☐ Known Personally | | |
| ☐ Acknowledgement | ☐ Drivers License | | Date Issued: | Expiration Date: |
| ☐ Other _____ | ☐ Other _____ | | | |

| Document Type | Date/Time Notarized: | Document Date: | Fee Charged: |
|---|---|---|---|

| Printed Name and Address of Witness: | Phone number: |
|---|---|
| | Email: |
| | Signer's Signature: |

| Comments | Record Number |
|---|---|

# NOTARY RECORD

| Printed Name and Address of Signer: | Phone number: | Thumb Print: |
|---|---|---|
| | Email: | |
| | Signer's Signature: | |

| **Service Performed** | **Identification** | ID Number: | |
|---|---|---|---|
| ☐ Jurat | ☐ ID Card  ☐ Credible Witness | Issued By: | |
| ☐ Oath | ☐ Passport  ☐ Known Personally | | |
| ☐ Acknowledgement | ☐ Drivers License | Date Issued: | Expiration Date: |
| ☐ Other _____ | ☐ Other _____ | | |

| Document Type | Date/Time Notarized: | Document Date: | Fee Charged: |
|---|---|---|---|

| Printed Name and Address of Witness: | Phone number: |
|---|---|
| | Email: |
| | Signer's Signature: |

| Comments | Record Number |
|---|---|

# NOTARY RECORD

| Printed Name and Address of Signer: | Phone number: | Thumb Print: |
|---|---|---|
| | Email: | |
| | Signer's Signature: | |

| **Service Performed** | **Identification** | ID Number: | |
|---|---|---|---|
| ☐ Jurat | ☐ ID Card  ☐ Credible Witness | Issued By: | |
| ☐ Oath | ☐ Passport  ☐ Known Personally | | |
| ☐ Acknowledgement | ☐ Drivers License | Date Issued: | Expiration Date: |
| ☐ Other _____ | ☐ Other _____ | | |

| Document Type | Date/Time Notarized: | Document Date: | Fee Charged: |
|---|---|---|---|

| Printed Name and Address of Witness: | Phone number: |
|---|---|
| | Email: |
| | Signer's Signature: |

| Comments | Record Number |
|---|---|

# NOTARY RECORD

| Printed Name and Address of Signer: | Phone number: | Thumb Print: |
|---|---|---|
| | Email: | |
| | Signer's Signature: | |

| Service Performed | Identification | | ID Number: | |
|---|---|---|---|---|
| ☐ Jurat | ☐ ID Card | ☐ Credible Witness | Issued By: | |
| ☐ Oath | ☐ Passport | ☐ Known Personally | | |
| ☐ Acknowledgement | ☐ Drivers License | | Date Issued: | Expiration Date: |
| ☐ Other _____ | ☐ Other _____ | | | |

| Document Type | Date/Time Notarized: | Document Date: | Fee Charged: |
|---|---|---|---|

| Printed Name and Address of Witness: | Phone number: |
|---|---|
| | Email: |
| | Signer's Signature: |

| Comments | Record Number |
|---|---|

# NOTARY RECORD

| Printed Name and Address of Signer: | Phone number: | Thumb Print: |
|---|---|---|
| | Email: | |
| | Signer's Signature: | |

| Service Performed | Identification | | ID Number: | |
|---|---|---|---|---|
| ☐ Jurat | ☐ ID Card | ☐ Credible Witness | Issued By: | |
| ☐ Oath | ☐ Passport | ☐ Known Personally | | |
| ☐ Acknowledgement | ☐ Drivers License | | Date Issued: | Expiration Date: |
| ☐ Other _____ | ☐ Other _____ | | | |

| Document Type | Date/Time Notarized: | Document Date: | Fee Charged: |
|---|---|---|---|

| Printed Name and Address of Witness: | Phone number: |
|---|---|
| | Email: |
| | Signer's Signature: |

| Comments | Record Number |
|---|---|

# NOTARY RECORD

| Printed Name and Address of Signer: | Phone number: | Thumb Print: |
|---|---|---|
| | Email: | |
| | Signer's Signature: | |

| **Service Performed** | **Identification** | ID Number: | |
|---|---|---|---|
| ☐ Jurat | ☐ ID Card ☐ Credible Witness | Issued By: | |
| ☐ Oath | ☐ Passport ☐ Known Personally | | |
| ☐ Acknowledgement | ☐ Drivers License | Date Issued: | Expiration Date: |
| ☐ Other _____ | ☐ Other _____ | | |

| Document Type | Date/Time Notarized: | Document Date: | Fee Charged: |
|---|---|---|---|

| Printed Name and Address of Witness: | Phone number: |
|---|---|
| | Email: |
| | Signer's Signature: |

| Comments | Record Number |
|---|---|

---

# NOTARY RECORD

| Printed Name and Address of Signer: | Phone number: | Thumb Print: |
|---|---|---|
| | Email: | |
| | Signer's Signature: | |

| **Service Performed** | **Identification** | ID Number: | |
|---|---|---|---|
| ☐ Jurat | ☐ ID Card ☐ Credible Witness | Issued By: | |
| ☐ Oath | ☐ Passport ☐ Known Personally | | |
| ☐ Acknowledgement | ☐ Drivers License | Date Issued: | Expiration Date: |
| ☐ Other _____ | ☐ Other _____ | | |

| Document Type | Date/Time Notarized: | Document Date: | Fee Charged: |
|---|---|---|---|

| Printed Name and Address of Witness: | Phone number: |
|---|---|
| | Email: |
| | Signer's Signature: |

| Comments | Record Number |
|---|---|

# NOTARY RECORD

| Printed Name and Address of Signer: | Phone number: | Thumb Print: |
|---|---|---|
| | Email: | |
| | Signer's Signature: | |

| **Service Performed** | **Identification** | ID Number: | |
|---|---|---|---|
| ☐ Jurat | ☐ ID Card  ☐ Credible Witness | Issued By: | |
| ☐ Oath | ☐ Passport  ☐ Known Personally | | |
| ☐ Acknowledgement | ☐ Drivers License | Date Issued: | Expiration Date: |
| ☐ Other _____ | ☐ Other _____ | | |

| Document Type | Date/Time Notarized: | Document Date: | Fee Charged: |
|---|---|---|---|

| Printed Name and Address of Witness: | Phone number: |
|---|---|
| | Email: |
| | Signer's Signature: |

| Comments | Record Number |
|---|---|

# NOTARY RECORD

| Printed Name and Address of Signer: | Phone number: | Thumb Print: |
|---|---|---|
| | Email: | |
| | Signer's Signature: | |

| **Service Performed** | **Identification** | ID Number: | |
|---|---|---|---|
| ☐ Jurat | ☐ ID Card  ☐ Credible Witness | Issued By: | |
| ☐ Oath | ☐ Passport  ☐ Known Personally | | |
| ☐ Acknowledgement | ☐ Drivers License | Date Issued: | Expiration Date: |
| ☐ Other _____ | ☐ Other _____ | | |

| Document Type | Date/Time Notarized: | Document Date: | Fee Charged: |
|---|---|---|---|

| Printed Name and Address of Witness: | Phone number: |
|---|---|
| | Email: |
| | Signer's Signature: |

| Comments | Record Number |
|---|---|

# NOTARY RECORD

| Printed Name and Address of Signer: | Phone number: | Thumb Print: |
|---|---|---|
| | Email: | |
| | Signer's Signature: | |

| **Service Performed** | **Identification** | | ID Number: | |
|---|---|---|---|---|
| ☐ Jurat | ☐ ID Card | ☐ Credible Witness | Issued By: | |
| ☐ Oath | ☐ Passport | ☐ Known Personally | | |
| ☐ Acknowledgement | ☐ Drivers License | | Date Issued: | Expiration Date: |
| ☐ Other _____ | ☐ Other _____ | | | |

| Document Type | Date/Time Notarized: | Document Date: | Fee Charged: |
|---|---|---|---|

| Printed Name and Address of Witness: | Phone number: |
|---|---|
| | Email: |
| | Signer's Signature: |

| Comments | Record Number |
|---|---|

---

# NOTARY RECORD

| Printed Name and Address of Signer: | Phone number: | Thumb Print: |
|---|---|---|
| | Email: | |
| | Signer's Signature: | |

| **Service Performed** | **Identification** | | ID Number: | |
|---|---|---|---|---|
| ☐ Jurat | ☐ ID Card | ☐ Credible Witness | Issued By: | |
| ☐ Oath | ☐ Passport | ☐ Known Personally | | |
| ☐ Acknowledgement | ☐ Drivers License | | Date Issued: | Expiration Date: |
| ☐ Other _____ | ☐ Other _____ | | | |

| Document Type | Date/Time Notarized: | Document Date: | Fee Charged: |
|---|---|---|---|

| Printed Name and Address of Witness: | Phone number: |
|---|---|
| | Email: |
| | Signer's Signature: |

| Comments | Record Number |
|---|---|

# NOTARY RECORD

| Printed Name and Address of Signer: | Phone number: | Thumb Print: |
|---|---|---|
| | Email: | |
| | Signer's Signature: | |

| **Service Performed** | **Identification** | ID Number: | |
|---|---|---|---|
| ☐ Jurat | ☐ ID Card  ☐ Credible Witness | Issued By: | |
| ☐ Oath | ☐ Passport  ☐ Known Personally | | |
| ☐ Acknowledgement | ☐ Drivers License | Date Issued: | Expiration Date: |
| ☐ Other _____ | ☐ Other _____ | | |

| Document Type | Date/Time Notarized: | Document Date: | Fee Charged: |
|---|---|---|---|

| Printed Name and Address of Witness: | Phone number: |
|---|---|
| | Email: |
| | Signer's Signature: |

| Comments | Record Number |
|---|---|

# NOTARY RECORD

| Printed Name and Address of Signer: | Phone number: | Thumb Print: |
|---|---|---|
| | Email: | |
| | Signer's Signature: | |

| **Service Performed** | **Identification** | ID Number: | |
|---|---|---|---|
| ☐ Jurat | ☐ ID Card  ☐ Credible Witness | Issued By: | |
| ☐ Oath | ☐ Passport  ☐ Known Personally | | |
| ☐ Acknowledgement | ☐ Drivers License | Date Issued: | Expiration Date: |
| ☐ Other _____ | ☐ Other _____ | | |

| Document Type | Date/Time Notarized: | Document Date: | Fee Charged: |
|---|---|---|---|

| Printed Name and Address of Witness: | Phone number: |
|---|---|
| | Email: |
| | Signer's Signature: |

| Comments | Record Number |
|---|---|

# NOTARY RECORD

| Printed Name and Address of Signer: | Phone number: | Thumb Print: |
|---|---|---|
| | Email: | |
| | Signer's Signature: | |

| Service Performed | Identification | ID Number: | |
|---|---|---|---|
| ☐ Jurat | ☐ ID Card  ☐ Credible Witness | Issued By: | |
| ☐ Oath | ☐ Passport  ☐ Known Personally | | |
| ☐ Acknowledgement | ☐ Drivers License | Date Issued: | Expiration Date: |
| ☐ Other _____ | ☐ Other _____ | | |

| Document Type | Date/Time Notarized: | Document Date: | Fee Charged: |
|---|---|---|---|

| Printed Name and Address of Witness: | Phone number: |
|---|---|
| | Email: |
| | Signer's Signature: |

| Comments | Record Number |
|---|---|

# NOTARY RECORD

| Printed Name and Address of Signer: | Phone number: | Thumb Print: |
|---|---|---|
| | Email: | |
| | Signer's Signature: | |

| Service Performed | Identification | ID Number: | |
|---|---|---|---|
| ☐ Jurat | ☐ ID Card  ☐ Credible Witness | Issued By: | |
| ☐ Oath | ☐ Passport  ☐ Known Personally | | |
| ☐ Acknowledgement | ☐ Drivers License | Date Issued: | Expiration Date: |
| ☐ Other _____ | ☐ Other _____ | | |

| Document Type | Date/Time Notarized: | Document Date: | Fee Charged: |
|---|---|---|---|

| Printed Name and Address of Witness: | Phone number: |
|---|---|
| | Email: |
| | Signer's Signature: |

| Comments | Record Number |
|---|---|

# NOTARY RECORD

| Printed Name and Address of Signer: | Phone number: | Thumb Print: |
|---|---|---|
| | Email: | |
| | Signer's Signature: | |

| Service Performed | Identification | | ID Number: | |
|---|---|---|---|---|
| ☐ Jurat | ☐ ID Card | ☐ Credible Witness | Issued By: | |
| ☐ Oath | ☐ Passport | ☐ Known Personally | | |
| ☐ Acknowledgement | ☐ Drivers License | | Date Issued: | Expiration Date: |
| ☐ Other _____ | ☐ Other _____ | | | |

| Document Type | Date/Time Notarized: | Document Date: | Fee Charged: |
|---|---|---|---|

| Printed Name and Address of Witness: | Phone number: |
|---|---|
| | Email: |
| | Signer's Signature: |

| Comments | Record Number |
|---|---|

# NOTARY RECORD

| Printed Name and Address of Signer: | Phone number: | Thumb Print: |
|---|---|---|
| | Email: | |
| | Signer's Signature: | |

| Service Performed | Identification | | ID Number: | |
|---|---|---|---|---|
| ☐ Jurat | ☐ ID Card | ☐ Credible Witness | Issued By: | |
| ☐ Oath | ☐ Passport | ☐ Known Personally | | |
| ☐ Acknowledgement | ☐ Drivers License | | Date Issued: | Expiration Date: |
| ☐ Other _____ | ☐ Other _____ | | | |

| Document Type | Date/Time Notarized: | Document Date: | Fee Charged: |
|---|---|---|---|

| Printed Name and Address of Witness: | Phone number: |
|---|---|
| | Email: |
| | Signer's Signature: |

| Comments | Record Number |
|---|---|

# NOTARY RECORD

| Printed Name and Address of Signer: | Phone number: | Thumb Print: |
|---|---|---|
| | Email: | |
| | Signer's Signature: | |

| Service Performed | Identification | ID Number: | |
|---|---|---|---|
| ☐ Jurat | ☐ ID Card ☐ Credible Witness | Issued By: | |
| ☐ Oath | ☐ Passport ☐ Known Personally | | |
| ☐ Acknowledgement | ☐ Drivers License | Date Issued: | Expiration Date: |
| ☐ Other _____ | ☐ Other _____ | | |

| Document Type | Date/Time Notarized: | Document Date: | Fee Charged: |
|---|---|---|---|

| Printed Name and Address of Witness: | Phone number: |
|---|---|
| | Email: |
| | Signer's Signature: |

| Comments | Record Number |
|---|---|

# NOTARY RECORD

| Printed Name and Address of Signer: | Phone number: | Thumb Print: |
|---|---|---|
| | Email: | |
| | Signer's Signature: | |

| Service Performed | Identification | ID Number: | |
|---|---|---|---|
| ☐ Jurat | ☐ ID Card ☐ Credible Witness | Issued By: | |
| ☐ Oath | ☐ Passport ☐ Known Personally | | |
| ☐ Acknowledgement | ☐ Drivers License | Date Issued: | Expiration Date: |
| ☐ Other _____ | ☐ Other _____ | | |

| Document Type | Date/Time Notarized: | Document Date: | Fee Charged: |
|---|---|---|---|

| Printed Name and Address of Witness: | Phone number: |
|---|---|
| | Email: |
| | Signer's Signature: |

| Comments | Record Number |
|---|---|

# NOTARY RECORD

| Printed Name and Address of Signer: | Phone number: | Thumb Print: |
|---|---|---|
| | Email: | |
| | Signer's Signature: | |

| Service Performed | Identification | ID Number: | |
|---|---|---|---|
| ☐ Jurat | ☐ ID Card  ☐ Credible Witness | Issued By: | |
| ☐ Oath | ☐ Passport  ☐ Known Personally | | |
| ☐ Acknowledgement | ☐ Drivers License | Date Issued: | Expiration Date: |
| ☐ Other _____ | ☐ Other _____ | | |

| Document Type | Date/Time Notarized: | Document Date: | Fee Charged: |
|---|---|---|---|

| Printed Name and Address of Witness: | Phone number: |
|---|---|
| | Email: |
| | Signer's Signature: |

| Comments | Record Number |
|---|---|

# NOTARY RECORD

| Printed Name and Address of Signer: | Phone number: | Thumb Print: |
|---|---|---|
| | Email: | |
| | Signer's Signature: | |

| Service Performed | Identification | ID Number: | |
|---|---|---|---|
| ☐ Jurat | ☐ ID Card  ☐ Credible Witness | Issued By: | |
| ☐ Oath | ☐ Passport  ☐ Known Personally | | |
| ☐ Acknowledgement | ☐ Drivers License | Date Issued: | Expiration Date: |
| ☐ Other _____ | ☐ Other _____ | | |

| Document Type | Date/Time Notarized: | Document Date: | Fee Charged: |
|---|---|---|---|

| Printed Name and Address of Witness: | Phone number: |
|---|---|
| | Email: |
| | Signer's Signature: |

| Comments | Record Number |
|---|---|

# NOTARY RECORD

| Printed Name and Address of Signer: | Phone number: | Thumb Print: |
|---|---|---|
| | Email: | |
| | Signer's Signature: | |

| Service Performed | Identification | ID Number: | |
|---|---|---|---|
| ☐ Jurat | ☐ ID Card  ☐ Credible Witness | Issued By: | |
| ☐ Oath | ☐ Passport  ☐ Known Personally | | |
| ☐ Acknowledgement | ☐ Drivers License | Date Issued: | Expiration Date: |
| ☐ Other _____ | ☐ Other _____ | | |

| Document Type | Date/Time Notarized: | Document Date: | Fee Charged: |
|---|---|---|---|

| Printed Name and Address of Witness: | Phone number: |
|---|---|
| | Email: |
| | Signer's Signature: |

| Comments | Record Number |
|---|---|

---

# NOTARY RECORD

| Printed Name and Address of Signer: | Phone number: | Thumb Print: |
|---|---|---|
| | Email: | |
| | Signer's Signature: | |

| Service Performed | Identification | ID Number: | |
|---|---|---|---|
| ☐ Jurat | ☐ ID Card  ☐ Credible Witness | Issued By: | |
| ☐ Oath | ☐ Passport  ☐ Known Personally | | |
| ☐ Acknowledgement | ☐ Drivers License | Date Issued: | Expiration Date: |
| ☐ Other _____ | ☐ Other _____ | | |

| Document Type | Date/Time Notarized: | Document Date: | Fee Charged: |
|---|---|---|---|

| Printed Name and Address of Witness: | Phone number: |
|---|---|
| | Email: |
| | Signer's Signature: |

| Comments | Record Number |
|---|---|

# NOTARY RECORD

**Printed Name and Address of Signer:**

Phone number:

Email:

Signer's Signature:

Thumb Print:

| Service Performed | Identification | | ID Number: | |
|---|---|---|---|---|
| ☐ Jurat | ☐ ID Card | ☐ Credible Witness | Issued By: | |
| ☐ Oath | ☐ Passport | ☐ Known Personally | | |
| ☐ Acknowledgement | ☐ Drivers License | | Date Issued: | Expiration Date: |
| ☐ Other _____ | ☐ Other _____ | | | |

| Document Type | Date/Time Notarized: | Document Date: | Fee Charged: |
|---|---|---|---|

**Printed Name and Address of Witness:**

Phone number:

Email:

Signer's Signature:

| Comments | Record Number |
|---|---|

---

# NOTARY RECORD

**Printed Name and Address of Signer:**

Phone number:

Email:

Signer's Signature:

Thumb Print:

| Service Performed | Identification | | ID Number: | |
|---|---|---|---|---|
| ☐ Jurat | ☐ ID Card | ☐ Credible Witness | Issued By: | |
| ☐ Oath | ☐ Passport | ☐ Known Personally | | |
| ☐ Acknowledgement | ☐ Drivers License | | Date Issued: | Expiration Date: |
| ☐ Other _____ | ☐ Other _____ | | | |

| Document Type | Date/Time Notarized: | Document Date: | Fee Charged: |
|---|---|---|---|

**Printed Name and Address of Witness:**

Phone number:

Email:

Signer's Signature:

| Comments | Record Number |
|---|---|

# NOTARY RECORD

| Printed Name and Address of Signer: | Phone number: | Thumb Print: |
|---|---|---|
| | Email: | |
| | Signer's Signature: | |

| Service Performed | Identification | ID Number: | |
|---|---|---|---|
| ☐ Jurat | ☐ ID Card    ☐ Credible Witness | Issued By: | |
| ☐ Oath | ☐ Passport    ☐ Known Personally | | |
| ☐ Acknowledgement | ☐ Drivers License | Date Issued: | Expiration Date: |
| ☐ Other _____ | ☐ Other _____ | | |

| Document Type | Date/Time Notarized: | Document Date: | Fee Charged: |
|---|---|---|---|

| Printed Name and Address of Witness: | Phone number: |
|---|---|
| | Email: |
| | Signer's Signature: |

| Comments | Record Number |
|---|---|

# NOTARY RECORD

| Printed Name and Address of Signer: | Phone number: | Thumb Print: |
|---|---|---|
| | Email: | |
| | Signer's Signature: | |

| Service Performed | Identification | ID Number: | |
|---|---|---|---|
| ☐ Jurat | ☐ ID Card    ☐ Credible Witness | Issued By: | |
| ☐ Oath | ☐ Passport    ☐ Known Personally | | |
| ☐ Acknowledgement | ☐ Drivers License | Date Issued: | Expiration Date: |
| ☐ Other _____ | ☐ Other _____ | | |

| Document Type | Date/Time Notarized: | Document Date: | Fee Charged: |
|---|---|---|---|

| Printed Name and Address of Witness: | Phone number: |
|---|---|
| | Email: |
| | Signer's Signature: |

| Comments | Record Number |
|---|---|

# NOTARY RECORD

| Printed Name and Address of Signer: | Phone number: | Thumb Print: |
|---|---|---|
| | Email: | |
| | Signer's Signature: | |

| **Service Performed** | **Identification** | ID Number: | |
|---|---|---|---|
| ☐ Jurat | ☐ ID Card    ☐ Credible Witness | Issued By: | |
| ☐ Oath | ☐ Passport    ☐ Known Personally | | |
| ☐ Acknowledgement | ☐ Drivers License | Date Issued: | Expiration Date: |
| ☐ Other _____ | ☐ Other _____ | | |

| Document Type | Date/Time Notarized: | Document Date: | Fee Charged: |
|---|---|---|---|

| Printed Name and Address of Witness: | Phone number: |
|---|---|
| | Email: |
| | Signer's Signature: |

| Comments | Record Number |
|---|---|

# NOTARY RECORD

| Printed Name and Address of Signer: | Phone number: | Thumb Print: |
|---|---|---|
| | Email: | |
| | Signer's Signature: | |

| **Service Performed** | **Identification** | ID Number: | |
|---|---|---|---|
| ☐ Jurat | ☐ ID Card    ☐ Credible Witness | Issued By: | |
| ☐ Oath | ☐ Passport    ☐ Known Personally | | |
| ☐ Acknowledgement | ☐ Drivers License | Date Issued: | Expiration Date: |
| ☐ Other _____ | ☐ Other _____ | | |

| Document Type | Date/Time Notarized: | Document Date: | Fee Charged: |
|---|---|---|---|

| Printed Name and Address of Witness: | Phone number: |
|---|---|
| | Email: |
| | Signer's Signature: |

| Comments | Record Number |
|---|---|

# NOTARY RECORD

**Printed Name and Address of Signer:**

Phone number:

Email:

Signer's Signature:

Thumb Print:

| Service Performed | Identification | | ID Number: | |
|---|---|---|---|---|
| ☐ Jurat | ☐ ID Card | ☐ Credible Witness | Issued By: | |
| ☐ Oath | ☐ Passport | ☐ Known Personally | | |
| ☐ Acknowledgement | ☐ Drivers License | | Date Issued: | Expiration Date: |
| ☐ Other _____ | ☐ Other _____ | | | |

| Document Type | Date/Time Notarized: | Document Date: | Fee Charged: |
|---|---|---|---|

**Printed Name and Address of Witness:**

Phone number:

Email:

Signer's Signature:

| Comments | Record Number |
|---|---|

---

# NOTARY RECORD

**Printed Name and Address of Signer:**

Phone number:

Email:

Signer's Signature:

Thumb Print:

| Service Performed | Identification | | ID Number: | |
|---|---|---|---|---|
| ☐ Jurat | ☐ ID Card | ☐ Credible Witness | Issued By: | |
| ☐ Oath | ☐ Passport | ☐ Known Personally | | |
| ☐ Acknowledgement | ☐ Drivers License | | Date Issued: | Expiration Date: |
| ☐ Other _____ | ☐ Other _____ | | | |

| Document Type | Date/Time Notarized: | Document Date: | Fee Charged: |
|---|---|---|---|

**Printed Name and Address of Witness:**

Phone number:

Email:

Signer's Signature:

| Comments | Record Number |
|---|---|

# NOTARY RECORD

| Printed Name and Address of Signer: | Phone number: | Thumb Print: |
|---|---|---|
| | Email: | |
| | Signer's Signature: | |

**Service Performed**

☐ Jurat
☐ Oath
☐ Acknowledgement
☐ Other _____

**Identification**

☐ ID Card          ☐ Credible Witness
☐ Passport        ☐ Known Personally
☐ Drivers License
☐ Other _____

| ID Number: | |
|---|---|
| Issued By: | |
| Date Issued: | Expiration Date: |

| Document Type | Date/Time Notarized: | Document Date: | Fee Charged: |
|---|---|---|---|

| Printed Name and Address of Witness: | Phone number: |
|---|---|
| | Email: |
| | Signer's Signature: |

| Comments | Record Number |
|---|---|

---

# NOTARY RECORD

| Printed Name and Address of Signer: | Phone number: | Thumb Print: |
|---|---|---|
| | Email: | |
| | Signer's Signature: | |

**Service Performed**

☐ Jurat
☐ Oath
☐ Acknowledgement
☐ Other _____

**Identification**

☐ ID Card          ☐ Credible Witness
☐ Passport        ☐ Known Personally
☐ Drivers License
☐ Other _____

| ID Number: | |
|---|---|
| Issued By: | |
| Date Issued: | Expiration Date: |

| Document Type | Date/Time Notarized: | Document Date: | Fee Charged: |
|---|---|---|---|

| Printed Name and Address of Witness: | Phone number: |
|---|---|
| | Email: |
| | Signer's Signature: |

| Comments | Record Number |
|---|---|

# NOTARY RECORD

**Printed Name and Address of Signer:**

Phone number:

Email:

Signer's Signature:

Thumb Print:

| **Service Performed** | **Identification** | ID Number: | |
|---|---|---|---|
| ☐ Jurat | ☐ ID Card   ☐ Credible Witness | Issued By: | |
| ☐ Oath | ☐ Passport   ☐ Known Personally | | |
| ☐ Acknowledgement | ☐ Drivers License | Date Issued: | Expiration Date: |
| ☐ Other _____ | ☐ Other _____ | | |
| Document Type | Date/Time Notarized: | Document Date: | Fee Charged: |

**Printed Name and Address of Witness:**

Phone number:

Email:

Signer's Signature:

Comments

Record Number

---

# NOTARY RECORD

**Printed Name and Address of Signer:**

Phone number:

Email:

Signer's Signature:

Thumb Print:

| **Service Performed** | **Identification** | ID Number: | |
|---|---|---|---|
| ☐ Jurat | ☐ ID Card   ☐ Credible Witness | Issued By: | |
| ☐ Oath | ☐ Passport   ☐ Known Personally | | |
| ☐ Acknowledgement | ☐ Drivers License | Date Issued: | Expiration Date: |
| ☐ Other _____ | ☐ Other _____ | | |
| Document Type | Date/Time Notarized: | Document Date: | Fee Charged: |

**Printed Name and Address of Witness:**

Phone number:

Email:

Signer's Signature:

Comments

Record Number

# NOTARY RECORD

| Printed Name and Address of Signer: | Phone number: | Thumb Print: |
|---|---|---|
| | Email: | |
| | Signer's Signature: | |

| Service Performed | Identification | ID Number: | |
|---|---|---|---|
| ☐ Jurat | ☐ ID Card ☐ Credible Witness | Issued By: | |
| ☐ Oath | ☐ Passport ☐ Known Personally | | |
| ☐ Acknowledgement | ☐ Drivers License | Date Issued: | Expiration Date: |
| ☐ Other _____ | ☐ Other _____ | | |

| Document Type | Date/Time Notarized: | Document Date: | Fee Charged: |
|---|---|---|---|

| Printed Name and Address of Witness: | Phone number: |
|---|---|
| | Email: |
| | Signer's Signature: |

| Comments | Record Number |
|---|---|

# NOTARY RECORD

| Printed Name and Address of Signer: | Phone number: | Thumb Print: |
|---|---|---|
| | Email: | |
| | Signer's Signature: | |

| Service Performed | Identification | ID Number: | |
|---|---|---|---|
| ☐ Jurat | ☐ ID Card ☐ Credible Witness | Issued By: | |
| ☐ Oath | ☐ Passport ☐ Known Personally | | |
| ☐ Acknowledgement | ☐ Drivers License | Date Issued: | Expiration Date: |
| ☐ Other _____ | ☐ Other _____ | | |

| Document Type | Date/Time Notarized: | Document Date: | Fee Charged: |
|---|---|---|---|

| Printed Name and Address of Witness: | Phone number: |
|---|---|
| | Email: |
| | Signer's Signature: |

| Comments | Record Number |
|---|---|

# NOTARY RECORD

| Printed Name and Address of Signer: | Phone number: | Thumb Print: |
|---|---|---|
| | Email: | |
| | Signer's Signature: | |

| **Service Performed** | **Identification** | ID Number: | |
|---|---|---|---|
| ☐ Jurat | ☐ ID Card  ☐ Credible Witness | Issued By: | |
| ☐ Oath | ☐ Passport  ☐ Known Personally | | |
| ☐ Acknowledgement | ☐ Drivers License | Date Issued: | Expiration Date: |
| ☐ Other _____ | ☐ Other _____ | | |

| Document Type | Date/Time Notarized: | Document Date: | Fee Charged: |
|---|---|---|---|

| Printed Name and Address of Witness: | Phone number: |
|---|---|
| | Email: |
| | Signer's Signature: |

| Comments | Record Number |
|---|---|

---

# NOTARY RECORD

| Printed Name and Address of Signer: | Phone number: | Thumb Print: |
|---|---|---|
| | Email: | |
| | Signer's Signature: | |

| **Service Performed** | **Identification** | ID Number: | |
|---|---|---|---|
| ☐ Jurat | ☐ ID Card  ☐ Credible Witness | Issued By: | |
| ☐ Oath | ☐ Passport  ☐ Known Personally | | |
| ☐ Acknowledgement | ☐ Drivers License | Date Issued: | Expiration Date: |
| ☐ Other _____ | ☐ Other _____ | | |

| Document Type | Date/Time Notarized: | Document Date: | Fee Charged: |
|---|---|---|---|

| Printed Name and Address of Witness: | Phone number: |
|---|---|
| | Email: |
| | Signer's Signature: |

| Comments | Record Number |
|---|---|

# NOTARY RECORD

| Printed Name and Address of Signer: | Phone number: | Thumb Print: |
|---|---|---|
| | Email: | |
| | Signer's Signature: | |

| Service Performed | Identification | ID Number: | |
|---|---|---|---|
| ☐ Jurat | ☐ ID Card ☐ Credible Witness | Issued By: | |
| ☐ Oath | ☐ Passport ☐ Known Personally | | |
| ☐ Acknowledgement | ☐ Drivers License | Date Issued: | Expiration Date: |
| ☐ Other _____ | ☐ Other _____ | | |

| Document Type | Date/Time Notarized: | Document Date: | Fee Charged: |
|---|---|---|---|

| Printed Name and Address of Witness: | Phone number: |
|---|---|
| | Email: |
| | Signer's Signature: |

| Comments | Record Number |
|---|---|

---

# NOTARY RECORD

| Printed Name and Address of Signer: | Phone number: | Thumb Print: |
|---|---|---|
| | Email: | |
| | Signer's Signature: | |

| Service Performed | Identification | ID Number: | |
|---|---|---|---|
| ☐ Jurat | ☐ ID Card ☐ Credible Witness | Issued By: | |
| ☐ Oath | ☐ Passport ☐ Known Personally | | |
| ☐ Acknowledgement | ☐ Drivers License | Date Issued: | Expiration Date: |
| ☐ Other _____ | ☐ Other _____ | | |

| Document Type | Date/Time Notarized: | Document Date: | Fee Charged: |
|---|---|---|---|

| Printed Name and Address of Witness: | Phone number: |
|---|---|
| | Email: |
| | Signer's Signature: |

| Comments | Record Number |
|---|---|

# NOTARY RECORD

| Printed Name and Address of Signer: | Phone number: | Thumb Print: |
|---|---|---|
| | Email: | |
| | Signer's Signature: | |

| **Service Performed** | **Identification** | ID Number: | |
|---|---|---|---|
| ☐ Jurat | ☐ ID Card     ☐ Credible Witness | Issued By: | |
| ☐ Oath | ☐ Passport   ☐ Known Personally | | |
| ☐ Acknowledgement | ☐ Drivers License | Date Issued: | Expiration Date: |
| ☐ Other _____ | ☐ Other _____ | | |

| Document Type | Date/Time Notarized: | Document Date: | Fee Charged: |
|---|---|---|---|

| Printed Name and Address of Witness: | Phone number: |
|---|---|
| | Email: |
| | Signer's Signature: |

| Comments | Record Number |
|---|---|

# NOTARY RECORD

| Printed Name and Address of Signer: | Phone number: | Thumb Print: |
|---|---|---|
| | Email: | |
| | Signer's Signature: | |

| **Service Performed** | **Identification** | ID Number: | |
|---|---|---|---|
| ☐ Jurat | ☐ ID Card     ☐ Credible Witness | Issued By: | |
| ☐ Oath | ☐ Passport   ☐ Known Personally | | |
| ☐ Acknowledgement | ☐ Drivers License | Date Issued: | Expiration Date: |
| ☐ Other _____ | ☐ Other _____ | | |

| Document Type | Date/Time Notarized: | Document Date: | Fee Charged: |
|---|---|---|---|

| Printed Name and Address of Witness: | Phone number: |
|---|---|
| | Email: |
| | Signer's Signature: |

| Comments | Record Number |
|---|---|

# NOTARY RECORD

| Printed Name and Address of Signer: | Phone number: | Thumb Print: |
|---|---|---|
| | Email: | |
| | Signer's Signature: | |

**Service Performed**

- ☐ Jurat
- ☐ Oath
- ☐ Acknowledgement
- ☐ Other _____

**Identification**

- ☐ ID Card
- ☐ Passport
- ☐ Drivers License
- ☐ Other _____
- ☐ Credible Witness
- ☐ Known Personally

| ID Number: | |
|---|---|
| Issued By: | |
| Date Issued: | Expiration Date: |

| Document Type | Date/Time Notarized: | Document Date: | Fee Charged: |
|---|---|---|---|

| Printed Name and Address of Witness: | Phone number: |
|---|---|
| | Email: |
| | Signer's Signature: |

| Comments | Record Number |
|---|---|

---

# NOTARY RECORD

| Printed Name and Address of Signer: | Phone number: | Thumb Print: |
|---|---|---|
| | Email: | |
| | Signer's Signature: | |

**Service Performed**

- ☐ Jurat
- ☐ Oath
- ☐ Acknowledgement
- ☐ Other _____

**Identification**

- ☐ ID Card
- ☐ Passport
- ☐ Drivers License
- ☐ Other _____
- ☐ Credible Witness
- ☐ Known Personally

| ID Number: | |
|---|---|
| Issued By: | |
| Date Issued: | Expiration Date: |

| Document Type | Date/Time Notarized: | Document Date: | Fee Charged: |
|---|---|---|---|

| Printed Name and Address of Witness: | Phone number: |
|---|---|
| | Email: |
| | Signer's Signature: |

| Comments | Record Number |
|---|---|

# NOTARY RECORD

| Printed Name and Address of Signer: | Phone number: | Thumb Print: |
|---|---|---|
| | Email: | |
| | Signer's Signature: | |

| **Service Performed** | **Identification** | ID Number: | |
|---|---|---|---|
| ☐ Jurat | ☐ ID Card   ☐ Credible Witness | Issued By: | |
| ☐ Oath | ☐ Passport   ☐ Known Personally | | |
| ☐ Acknowledgement | ☐ Drivers License | Date Issued: | Expiration Date: |
| ☐ Other _____ | ☐ Other _____ | | |

| Document Type | Date/Time Notarized: | Document Date: | Fee Charged: |
|---|---|---|---|

| Printed Name and Address of Witness: | Phone number: |
|---|---|
| | Email: |
| | Signer's Signature: |

| Comments | Record Number |
|---|---|

# NOTARY RECORD

| Printed Name and Address of Signer: | Phone number: | Thumb Print: |
|---|---|---|
| | Email: | |
| | Signer's Signature: | |

| **Service Performed** | **Identification** | ID Number: | |
|---|---|---|---|
| ☐ Jurat | ☐ ID Card   ☐ Credible Witness | Issued By: | |
| ☐ Oath | ☐ Passport   ☐ Known Personally | | |
| ☐ Acknowledgement | ☐ Drivers License | Date Issued: | Expiration Date: |
| ☐ Other _____ | ☐ Other _____ | | |

| Document Type | Date/Time Notarized: | Document Date: | Fee Charged: |
|---|---|---|---|

| Printed Name and Address of Witness: | Phone number: |
|---|---|
| | Email: |
| | Signer's Signature: |

| Comments | Record Number |
|---|---|

# NOTARY RECORD

| Printed Name and Address of Signer: | Phone number: | Thumb Print: |
|---|---|---|
| | Email: | |
| | Signer's Signature: | |

| **Service Performed** | **Identification** | | ID Number: | |
|---|---|---|---|---|
| ☐ Jurat | ☐ ID Card | ☐ Credible Witness | Issued By: | |
| ☐ Oath | ☐ Passport | ☐ Known Personally | | |
| ☐ Acknowledgement | ☐ Drivers License | | Date Issued: | Expiration Date: |
| ☐ Other _____ | ☐ Other _____ | | | |

| Document Type | Date/Time Notarized: | Document Date: | Fee Charged: |
|---|---|---|---|

| Printed Name and Address of Witness: | Phone number: |
|---|---|
| | Email: |
| | Signer's Signature: |

| Comments | Record Number |
|---|---|

# NOTARY RECORD

| Printed Name and Address of Signer: | Phone number: | Thumb Print: |
|---|---|---|
| | Email: | |
| | Signer's Signature: | |

| **Service Performed** | **Identification** | | ID Number: | |
|---|---|---|---|---|
| ☐ Jurat | ☐ ID Card | ☐ Credible Witness | Issued By: | |
| ☐ Oath | ☐ Passport | ☐ Known Personally | | |
| ☐ Acknowledgement | ☐ Drivers License | | Date Issued: | Expiration Date: |
| ☐ Other _____ | ☐ Other _____ | | | |

| Document Type | Date/Time Notarized: | Document Date: | Fee Charged: |
|---|---|---|---|

| Printed Name and Address of Witness: | Phone number: |
|---|---|
| | Email: |
| | Signer's Signature: |

| Comments | Record Number |
|---|---|

# NOTARY RECORD

| Printed Name and Address of Signer: | Phone number: | Thumb Print: |
|---|---|---|
| | Email: | |
| | Signer's Signature: | |

| **Service Performed** | **Identification** | ID Number: | |
|---|---|---|---|
| ☐ Jurat | ☐ ID Card ☐ Credible Witness | Issued By: | |
| ☐ Oath | ☐ Passport ☐ Known Personally | | |
| ☐ Acknowledgement | ☐ Drivers License | Date Issued: | Expiration Date: |
| ☐ Other _____ | ☐ Other _____ | | |

| Document Type | Date/Time Notarized: | Document Date: | Fee Charged: |
|---|---|---|---|

| Printed Name and Address of Witness: | Phone number: |
|---|---|
| | Email: |
| | Signer's Signature: |

| Comments | Record Number |
|---|---|

# NOTARY RECORD

| Printed Name and Address of Signer: | Phone number: | Thumb Print: |
|---|---|---|
| | Email: | |
| | Signer's Signature: | |

| **Service Performed** | **Identification** | ID Number: | |
|---|---|---|---|
| ☐ Jurat | ☐ ID Card ☐ Credible Witness | Issued By: | |
| ☐ Oath | ☐ Passport ☐ Known Personally | | |
| ☐ Acknowledgement | ☐ Drivers License | Date Issued: | Expiration Date: |
| ☐ Other _____ | ☐ Other _____ | | |

| Document Type | Date/Time Notarized: | Document Date: | Fee Charged: |
|---|---|---|---|

| Printed Name and Address of Witness: | Phone number: |
|---|---|
| | Email: |
| | Signer's Signature: |

| Comments | Record Number |
|---|---|

# NOTARY RECORD

| Printed Name and Address of Signer: | Phone number: | Thumb Print: |
|---|---|---|
| | Email: | |
| | Signer's Signature: | |

**Service Performed**

☐ Jurat
☐ Oath
☐ Acknowledgement
☐ Other _____

**Identification**

☐ ID Card        ☐ Credible Witness
☐ Passport       ☐ Known Personally
☐ Drivers License
☐ Other _____

| ID Number: | |
|---|---|
| Issued By: | |
| Date Issued: | Expiration Date: |

| Document Type | Date/Time Notarized: | Document Date: | Fee Charged: |
|---|---|---|---|

| Printed Name and Address of Witness: | Phone number: |
|---|---|
| | Email: |
| | Signer's Signature: |

| Comments | Record Number |
|---|---|

# NOTARY RECORD

| Printed Name and Address of Signer: | Phone number: | Thumb Print: |
|---|---|---|
| | Email: | |
| | Signer's Signature: | |

**Service Performed**

☐ Jurat
☐ Oath
☐ Acknowledgement
☐ Other _____

**Identification**

☐ ID Card        ☐ Credible Witness
☐ Passport       ☐ Known Personally
☐ Drivers License
☐ Other _____

| ID Number: | |
|---|---|
| Issued By: | |
| Date Issued: | Expiration Date: |

| Document Type | Date/Time Notarized: | Document Date: | Fee Charged: |
|---|---|---|---|

| Printed Name and Address of Witness: | Phone number: |
|---|---|
| | Email: |
| | Signer's Signature: |

| Comments | Record Number |
|---|---|

# NOTARY RECORD

**Printed Name and Address of Signer:**

| Phone number: |
| Email: |
| Signer's Signature: |

Thumb Print:

## Service Performed
- ☐ Jurat
- ☐ Oath
- ☐ Acknowledgement
- ☐ Other _____

## Identification
- ☐ ID Card
- ☐ Passport
- ☐ Drivers License
- ☐ Other _____
- ☐ Credible Witness
- ☐ Known Personally

ID Number:

Issued By:

Date Issued:

Expiration Date:

| Document Type | Date/Time Notarized: | Document Date: | Fee Charged: |

**Printed Name and Address of Witness:**

| Phone number: |
| Email: |
| Signer's Signature: |

Comments

Record Number

---

# NOTARY RECORD

**Printed Name and Address of Signer:**

| Phone number: |
| Email: |
| Signer's Signature: |

Thumb Print:

## Service Performed
- ☐ Jurat
- ☐ Oath
- ☐ Acknowledgement
- ☐ Other _____

## Identification
- ☐ ID Card
- ☐ Passport
- ☐ Drivers License
- ☐ Other _____
- ☐ Credible Witness
- ☐ Known Personally

ID Number:

Issued By:

Date Issued:

Expiration Date:

| Document Type | Date/Time Notarized: | Document Date: | Fee Charged: |

**Printed Name and Address of Witness:**

| Phone number: |
| Email: |
| Signer's Signature: |

Comments

Record Number

# NOTARY RECORD

| Printed Name and Address of Signer: | Phone number: | Thumb Print: |
|---|---|---|
| | Email: | |
| | Signer's Signature: | |

| **Service Performed** | **Identification** | | ID Number: | |
|---|---|---|---|---|
| ☐ Jurat | ☐ ID Card | ☐ Credible Witness | | |
| ☐ Oath | ☐ Passport | ☐ Known Personally | Issued By: | |
| ☐ Acknowledgement | ☐ Drivers License | | | |
| ☐ Other _____ | ☐ Other _____ | | Date Issued: | Expiration Date: |

| Document Type | Date/Time Notarized: | Document Date: | Fee Charged: |
|---|---|---|---|

| Printed Name and Address of Witness: | Phone number: |
|---|---|
| | Email: |
| | Signer's Signature: |

| Comments | Record Number |
|---|---|

---

# NOTARY RECORD

| Printed Name and Address of Signer: | Phone number: | Thumb Print: |
|---|---|---|
| | Email: | |
| | Signer's Signature: | |

| **Service Performed** | **Identification** | | ID Number: | |
|---|---|---|---|---|
| ☐ Jurat | ☐ ID Card | ☐ Credible Witness | | |
| ☐ Oath | ☐ Passport | ☐ Known Personally | Issued By: | |
| ☐ Acknowledgement | ☐ Drivers License | | | |
| ☐ Other _____ | ☐ Other _____ | | Date Issued: | Expiration Date: |

| Document Type | Date/Time Notarized: | Document Date: | Fee Charged: |
|---|---|---|---|

| Printed Name and Address of Witness: | Phone number: |
|---|---|
| | Email: |
| | Signer's Signature: |

| Comments | Record Number |
|---|---|

# NOTARY RECORD

| Printed Name and Address of Signer: | Phone number: | Thumb Print: |
|---|---|---|
| | Email: | |
| | Signer's Signature: | |

| **Service Performed** | **Identification** | | ID Number: | |
|---|---|---|---|---|
| ☐ Jurat | ☐ ID Card | ☐ Credible Witness | Issued By: | |
| ☐ Oath | ☐ Passport | ☐ Known Personally | | |
| ☐ Acknowledgement | ☐ Drivers License | | Date Issued: | Expiration Date: |
| ☐ Other _____ | ☐ Other _____ | | | |

| Document Type | Date/Time Notarized: | Document Date: | Fee Charged: |
|---|---|---|---|

| Printed Name and Address of Witness: | Phone number: |
|---|---|
| | Email: |
| | Signer's Signature: |

| Comments | Record Number |
|---|---|

# NOTARY RECORD

| Printed Name and Address of Signer: | Phone number: | Thumb Print: |
|---|---|---|
| | Email: | |
| | Signer's Signature: | |

| **Service Performed** | **Identification** | | ID Number: | |
|---|---|---|---|---|
| ☐ Jurat | ☐ ID Card | ☐ Credible Witness | Issued By: | |
| ☐ Oath | ☐ Passport | ☐ Known Personally | | |
| ☐ Acknowledgement | ☐ Drivers License | | Date Issued: | Expiration Date: |
| ☐ Other _____ | ☐ Other _____ | | | |

| Document Type | Date/Time Notarized: | Document Date: | Fee Charged: |
|---|---|---|---|

| Printed Name and Address of Witness: | Phone number: |
|---|---|
| | Email: |
| | Signer's Signature: |

| Comments | Record Number |
|---|---|

# NOTARY RECORD

| Printed Name and Address of Signer: | Phone number: | Thumb Print: |
|---|---|---|
| | Email: | |
| | Signer's Signature: | |

| **Service Performed** | **Identification** | ID Number: | |
|---|---|---|---|
| ☐ Jurat | ☐ ID Card    ☐ Credible Witness | Issued By: | |
| ☐ Oath | ☐ Passport    ☐ Known Personally | | |
| ☐ Acknowledgement | ☐ Drivers License | Date Issued: | Expiration Date: |
| ☐ Other _____ | ☐ Other _____ | | |

| Document Type | Date/Time Notarized: | Document Date: | Fee Charged: |
|---|---|---|---|

| Printed Name and Address of Witness: | Phone number: |
|---|---|
| | Email: |
| | Signer's Signature: |

| Comments | Record Number |
|---|---|

# NOTARY RECORD

| Printed Name and Address of Signer: | Phone number: | Thumb Print: |
|---|---|---|
| | Email: | |
| | Signer's Signature: | |

| **Service Performed** | **Identification** | ID Number: | |
|---|---|---|---|
| ☐ Jurat | ☐ ID Card    ☐ Credible Witness | Issued By: | |
| ☐ Oath | ☐ Passport    ☐ Known Personally | | |
| ☐ Acknowledgement | ☐ Drivers License | Date Issued: | Expiration Date: |
| ☐ Other _____ | ☐ Other _____ | | |

| Document Type | Date/Time Notarized: | Document Date: | Fee Charged: |
|---|---|---|---|

| Printed Name and Address of Witness: | Phone number: |
|---|---|
| | Email: |
| | Signer's Signature: |

| Comments | Record Number |
|---|---|

# NOTARY RECORD

| Printed Name and Address of Signer: | Phone number: | Thumb Print: |
|---|---|---|
| | Email: | |
| | Signer's Signature: | |

| Service Performed | Identification | ID Number: | |
|---|---|---|---|
| ☐ Jurat | ☐ ID Card   ☐ Credible Witness | Issued By: | |
| ☐ Oath | ☐ Passport   ☐ Known Personally | | |
| ☐ Acknowledgement | ☐ Drivers License | Date Issued: | Expiration Date: |
| ☐ Other _____ | ☐ Other _____ | | |

| Document Type | Date/Time Notarized: | Document Date: | Fee Charged: |
|---|---|---|---|

| Printed Name and Address of Witness: | Phone number: |
|---|---|
| | Email: |
| | Signer's Signature: |

| Comments | Record Number |
|---|---|

---

# NOTARY RECORD

| Printed Name and Address of Signer: | Phone number: | Thumb Print: |
|---|---|---|
| | Email: | |
| | Signer's Signature: | |

| Service Performed | Identification | ID Number: | |
|---|---|---|---|
| ☐ Jurat | ☐ ID Card   ☐ Credible Witness | Issued By: | |
| ☐ Oath | ☐ Passport   ☐ Known Personally | | |
| ☐ Acknowledgement | ☐ Drivers License | Date Issued: | Expiration Date: |
| ☐ Other _____ | ☐ Other _____ | | |

| Document Type | Date/Time Notarized: | Document Date: | Fee Charged: |
|---|---|---|---|

| Printed Name and Address of Witness: | Phone number: |
|---|---|
| | Email: |
| | Signer's Signature: |

| Comments | Record Number |
|---|---|

# NOTARY RECORD

| Printed Name and Address of Signer: | Phone number: | Thumb Print: |
|---|---|---|
| | Email: | |
| | Signer's Signature: | |

| **Service Performed** | **Identification** | | ID Number: | |
|---|---|---|---|---|
| ☐ Jurat | ☐ ID Card | ☐ Credible Witness | | |
| ☐ Oath | ☐ Passport | ☐ Known Personally | Issued By: | |
| ☐ Acknowledgement | ☐ Drivers License | | | |
| ☐ Other _____ | ☐ Other _____ | | Date Issued: | Expiration Date: |

| Document Type | Date/Time Notarized: | Document Date: | Fee Charged: |
|---|---|---|---|

| Printed Name and Address of Witness: | Phone number: |
|---|---|
| | Email: |
| | Signer's Signature: |

| Comments | Record Number |
|---|---|

# NOTARY RECORD

| Printed Name and Address of Signer: | Phone number: | Thumb Print: |
|---|---|---|
| | Email: | |
| | Signer's Signature: | |

| **Service Performed** | **Identification** | | ID Number: | |
|---|---|---|---|---|
| ☐ Jurat | ☐ ID Card | ☐ Credible Witness | | |
| ☐ Oath | ☐ Passport | ☐ Known Personally | Issued By: | |
| ☐ Acknowledgement | ☐ Drivers License | | | |
| ☐ Other _____ | ☐ Other _____ | | Date Issued: | Expiration Date: |

| Document Type | Date/Time Notarized: | Document Date: | Fee Charged: |
|---|---|---|---|

| Printed Name and Address of Witness: | Phone number: |
|---|---|
| | Email: |
| | Signer's Signature: |

| Comments | Record Number |
|---|---|

# NOTARY RECORD

| Printed Name and Address of Signer: | Phone number: | Thumb Print: |
|---|---|---|
| | Email: | |
| | Signer's Signature: | |

| **Service Performed** | **Identification** | ID Number: | |
|---|---|---|---|
| ☐ Jurat | ☐ ID Card  ☐ Credible Witness | Issued By: | |
| ☐ Oath | ☐ Passport  ☐ Known Personally | | |
| ☐ Acknowledgement | ☐ Drivers License | Date Issued: | Expiration Date: |
| ☐ Other _____ | ☐ Other _____ | | |

| Document Type | Date/Time Notarized: | Document Date: | Fee Charged: |
|---|---|---|---|

| Printed Name and Address of Witness: | Phone number: |
|---|---|
| | Email: |
| | Signer's Signature: |

| Comments | Record Number |
|---|---|

# NOTARY RECORD

| Printed Name and Address of Signer: | Phone number: | Thumb Print: |
|---|---|---|
| | Email: | |
| | Signer's Signature: | |

| **Service Performed** | **Identification** | ID Number: | |
|---|---|---|---|
| ☐ Jurat | ☐ ID Card  ☐ Credible Witness | Issued By: | |
| ☐ Oath | ☐ Passport  ☐ Known Personally | | |
| ☐ Acknowledgement | ☐ Drivers License | Date Issued: | Expiration Date: |
| ☐ Other _____ | ☐ Other _____ | | |

| Document Type | Date/Time Notarized: | Document Date: | Fee Charged: |
|---|---|---|---|

| Printed Name and Address of Witness: | Phone number: |
|---|---|
| | Email: |
| | Signer's Signature: |

| Comments | Record Number |
|---|---|

# NOTARY RECORD

| Printed Name and Address of Signer: | Phone number: | Thumb Print: |
|---|---|---|
| | Email: | |
| | Signer's Signature: | |

| Service Performed | Identification | | ID Number: | |
|---|---|---|---|---|
| ☐ Jurat | ☐ ID Card | ☐ Credible Witness | Issued By: | |
| ☐ Oath | ☐ Passport | ☐ Known Personally | | |
| ☐ Acknowledgement | ☐ Drivers License | | Date Issued: | Expiration Date: |
| ☐ Other _____ | ☐ Other _____ | | | |

| Document Type | Date/Time Notarized: | Document Date: | Fee Charged: |
|---|---|---|---|

| Printed Name and Address of Witness: | Phone number: |
|---|---|
| | Email: |
| | Signer's Signature: |

| Comments | Record Number |
|---|---|

# NOTARY RECORD

| Printed Name and Address of Signer: | Phone number: | Thumb Print: |
|---|---|---|
| | Email: | |
| | Signer's Signature: | |

| Service Performed | Identification | | ID Number: | |
|---|---|---|---|---|
| ☐ Jurat | ☐ ID Card | ☐ Credible Witness | Issued By: | |
| ☐ Oath | ☐ Passport | ☐ Known Personally | | |
| ☐ Acknowledgement | ☐ Drivers License | | Date Issued: | Expiration Date: |
| ☐ Other _____ | ☐ Other _____ | | | |

| Document Type | Date/Time Notarized: | Document Date: | Fee Charged: |
|---|---|---|---|

| Printed Name and Address of Witness: | Phone number: |
|---|---|
| | Email: |
| | Signer's Signature: |

| Comments | Record Number |
|---|---|

# NOTARY RECORD

| Printed Name and Address of Signer: | Phone number: | Thumb Print: |
|---|---|---|
| | Email: | |
| | Signer's Signature: | |

| Service Performed | Identification | | ID Number: | |
|---|---|---|---|---|
| ☐ Jurat | ☐ ID Card | ☐ Credible Witness | Issued By: | |
| ☐ Oath | ☐ Passport | ☐ Known Personally | | |
| ☐ Acknowledgement | ☐ Drivers License | | Date Issued: | Expiration Date: |
| ☐ Other _____ | ☐ Other _____ | | | |

| Document Type | Date/Time Notarized: | Document Date: | Fee Charged: |
|---|---|---|---|

| Printed Name and Address of Witness: | Phone number: |
|---|---|
| | Email: |
| | Signer's Signature: |

| Comments | Record Number |
|---|---|

# NOTARY RECORD

| Printed Name and Address of Signer: | Phone number: | Thumb Print: |
|---|---|---|
| | Email: | |
| | Signer's Signature: | |

| Service Performed | Identification | | ID Number: | |
|---|---|---|---|---|
| ☐ Jurat | ☐ ID Card | ☐ Credible Witness | Issued By: | |
| ☐ Oath | ☐ Passport | ☐ Known Personally | | |
| ☐ Acknowledgement | ☐ Drivers License | | Date Issued: | Expiration Date: |
| ☐ Other _____ | ☐ Other _____ | | | |

| Document Type | Date/Time Notarized: | Document Date: | Fee Charged: |
|---|---|---|---|

| Printed Name and Address of Witness: | Phone number: |
|---|---|
| | Email: |
| | Signer's Signature: |

| Comments | Record Number |
|---|---|

# NOTARY RECORD

| Printed Name and Address of Signer: | Phone number: | Thumb Print: |
|---|---|---|
| | Email: | |
| | Signer's Signature: | |

| Service Performed | Identification | | ID Number: | |
|---|---|---|---|---|
| ☐ Jurat | ☐ ID Card | ☐ Credible Witness | Issued By: | |
| ☐ Oath | ☐ Passport | ☐ Known Personally | | |
| ☐ Acknowledgement | ☐ Drivers License | | Date Issued: | Expiration Date: |
| ☐ Other _____ | ☐ Other _____ | | | |

| Document Type | Date/Time Notarized: | Document Date: | Fee Charged: |
|---|---|---|---|

| Printed Name and Address of Witness: | Phone number: |
|---|---|
| | Email: |
| | Signer's Signature: |

| Comments | Record Number |
|---|---|

# NOTARY RECORD

| Printed Name and Address of Signer: | Phone number: | Thumb Print: |
|---|---|---|
| | Email: | |
| | Signer's Signature: | |

| Service Performed | Identification | | ID Number: | |
|---|---|---|---|---|
| ☐ Jurat | ☐ ID Card | ☐ Credible Witness | Issued By: | |
| ☐ Oath | ☐ Passport | ☐ Known Personally | | |
| ☐ Acknowledgement | ☐ Drivers License | | Date Issued: | Expiration Date: |
| ☐ Other _____ | ☐ Other _____ | | | |

| Document Type | Date/Time Notarized: | Document Date: | Fee Charged: |
|---|---|---|---|

| Printed Name and Address of Witness: | Phone number: |
|---|---|
| | Email: |
| | Signer's Signature: |

| Comments | Record Number |
|---|---|

# NOTARY RECORD

**Printed Name and Address of Signer:**

Phone number:

Email:

Signer's Signature:

Thumb Print:

**Service Performed**
- ☐ Jurat
- ☐ Oath
- ☐ Acknowledgement
- ☐ Other _____

**Identification**
- ☐ ID Card
- ☐ Passport
- ☐ Drivers License
- ☐ Other _____
- ☐ Credible Witness
- ☐ Known Personally

ID Number:

Issued By:

Date Issued:

Expiration Date:

Document Type

Date/Time Notarized:

Document Date:

Fee Charged:

**Printed Name and Address of Witness:**

Phone number:

Email:

Signer's Signature:

Comments

Record Number

# NOTARY RECORD

**Printed Name and Address of Signer:**

Phone number:

Email:

Signer's Signature:

Thumb Print:

**Service Performed**
- ☐ Jurat
- ☐ Oath
- ☐ Acknowledgement
- ☐ Other _____

**Identification**
- ☐ ID Card
- ☐ Passport
- ☐ Drivers License
- ☐ Other _____
- ☐ Credible Witness
- ☐ Known Personally

ID Number:

Issued By:

Date Issued:

Expiration Date:

Document Type

Date/Time Notarized:

Document Date:

Fee Charged:

**Printed Name and Address of Witness:**

Phone number:

Email:

Signer's Signature:

Comments

Record Number

# NOTARY RECORD

| Printed Name and Address of Signer: | Phone number: | Thumb Print: |
|---|---|---|
| | Email: | |
| | Signer's Signature: | |

| Service Performed | Identification | | ID Number: | |
|---|---|---|---|---|
| ☐ Jurat | ☐ ID Card | ☐ Credible Witness | Issued By: | |
| ☐ Oath | ☐ Passport | ☐ Known Personally | | |
| ☐ Acknowledgement | ☐ Drivers License | | Date Issued: | Expiration Date: |
| ☐ Other _____ | ☐ Other _____ | | | |

| Document Type | Date/Time Notarized: | Document Date: | Fee Charged: |
|---|---|---|---|

| Printed Name and Address of Witness: | Phone number: |
|---|---|
| | Email: |
| | Signer's Signature: |

| Comments | Record Number |
|---|---|

# NOTARY RECORD

| Printed Name and Address of Signer: | Phone number: | Thumb Print: |
|---|---|---|
| | Email: | |
| | Signer's Signature: | |

| Service Performed | Identification | | ID Number: | |
|---|---|---|---|---|
| ☐ Jurat | ☐ ID Card | ☐ Credible Witness | Issued By: | |
| ☐ Oath | ☐ Passport | ☐ Known Personally | | |
| ☐ Acknowledgement | ☐ Drivers License | | Date Issued: | Expiration Date: |
| ☐ Other _____ | ☐ Other _____ | | | |

| Document Type | Date/Time Notarized: | Document Date: | Fee Charged: |
|---|---|---|---|

| Printed Name and Address of Witness: | Phone number: |
|---|---|
| | Email: |
| | Signer's Signature: |

| Comments | Record Number |
|---|---|

# NOTARY RECORD

| Printed Name and Address of Signer: | Phone number: | Thumb Print: |
|---|---|---|
| | Email: | |
| | Signer's Signature: | |

| **Service Performed** | **Identification** | ID Number: | |
|---|---|---|---|
| ☐ Jurat | ☐ ID Card  ☐ Credible Witness | Issued By: | |
| ☐ Oath | ☐ Passport  ☐ Known Personally | | |
| ☐ Acknowledgement | ☐ Drivers License | Date Issued: | Expiration Date: |
| ☐ Other _____ | ☐ Other _____ | | |

| Document Type | Date/Time Notarized: | Document Date: | Fee Charged: |
|---|---|---|---|

| Printed Name and Address of Witness: | Phone number: |
|---|---|
| | Email: |
| | Signer's Signature: |

| Comments | Record Number |
|---|---|

# NOTARY RECORD

| Printed Name and Address of Signer: | Phone number: | Thumb Print: |
|---|---|---|
| | Email: | |
| | Signer's Signature: | |

| **Service Performed** | **Identification** | ID Number: | |
|---|---|---|---|
| ☐ Jurat | ☐ ID Card  ☐ Credible Witness | Issued By: | |
| ☐ Oath | ☐ Passport  ☐ Known Personally | | |
| ☐ Acknowledgement | ☐ Drivers License | Date Issued: | Expiration Date: |
| ☐ Other _____ | ☐ Other _____ | | |

| Document Type | Date/Time Notarized: | Document Date: | Fee Charged: |
|---|---|---|---|

| Printed Name and Address of Witness: | Phone number: |
|---|---|
| | Email: |
| | Signer's Signature: |

| Comments | Record Number |
|---|---|

# NOTARY RECORD

**Printed Name and Address of Signer:**

Phone number:

Email:

Signer's Signature:

Thumb Print:

| **Service Performed** | **Identification** | | ID Number: | |
|---|---|---|---|---|
| ☐ Jurat | ☐ ID Card | ☐ Credible Witness | Issued By: | |
| ☐ Oath | ☐ Passport | ☐ Known Personally | | |
| ☐ Acknowledgement | ☐ Drivers License | | Date Issued: | Expiration Date: |
| ☐ Other _____ | ☐ Other _____ | | | |

| Document Type | Date/Time Notarized: | Document Date: | Fee Charged: |
|---|---|---|---|

**Printed Name and Address of Witness:**

Phone number:

Email:

Signer's Signature:

| Comments | Record Number |
|---|---|

---

# NOTARY RECORD

**Printed Name and Address of Signer:**

Phone number:

Email:

Signer's Signature:

Thumb Print:

| **Service Performed** | **Identification** | | ID Number: | |
|---|---|---|---|---|
| ☐ Jurat | ☐ ID Card | ☐ Credible Witness | Issued By: | |
| ☐ Oath | ☐ Passport | ☐ Known Personally | | |
| ☐ Acknowledgement | ☐ Drivers License | | Date Issued: | Expiration Date: |
| ☐ Other _____ | ☐ Other _____ | | | |

| Document Type | Date/Time Notarized: | Document Date: | Fee Charged: |
|---|---|---|---|

**Printed Name and Address of Witness:**

Phone number:

Email:

Signer's Signature:

| Comments | Record Number |
|---|---|

# NOTARY RECORD

| Printed Name and Address of Signer: | Phone number: | Thumb Print: |
|---|---|---|
| | Email: | |
| | Signer's Signature: | |

| Service Performed | Identification | ID Number: | |
|---|---|---|---|
| ☐ Jurat | ☐ ID Card  ☐ Credible Witness | Issued By: | |
| ☐ Oath | ☐ Passport  ☐ Known Personally | | |
| ☐ Acknowledgement | ☐ Drivers License | Date Issued: | Expiration Date: |
| ☐ Other _____ | ☐ Other _____ | | |

| Document Type | Date/Time Notarized: | Document Date: | Fee Charged: |
|---|---|---|---|

| Printed Name and Address of Witness: | Phone number: |
|---|---|
| | Email: |
| | Signer's Signature: |

| Comments | Record Number |
|---|---|

---

# NOTARY RECORD

| Printed Name and Address of Signer: | Phone number: | Thumb Print: |
|---|---|---|
| | Email: | |
| | Signer's Signature: | |

| Service Performed | Identification | ID Number: | |
|---|---|---|---|
| ☐ Jurat | ☐ ID Card  ☐ Credible Witness | Issued By: | |
| ☐ Oath | ☐ Passport  ☐ Known Personally | | |
| ☐ Acknowledgement | ☐ Drivers License | Date Issued: | Expiration Date: |
| ☐ Other _____ | ☐ Other _____ | | |

| Document Type | Date/Time Notarized: | Document Date: | Fee Charged: |
|---|---|---|---|

| Printed Name and Address of Witness: | Phone number: |
|---|---|
| | Email: |
| | Signer's Signature: |

| Comments | Record Number |
|---|---|

# NOTARY RECORD

| Printed Name and Address of Signer: | Phone number: | Thumb Print: |
|---|---|---|
| | Email: | |
| | Signer's Signature: | |

| **Service Performed** | **Identification** | ID Number: | |
|---|---|---|---|
| ☐ Jurat | ☐ ID Card  ☐ Credible Witness | Issued By: | |
| ☐ Oath | ☐ Passport  ☐ Known Personally | | |
| ☐ Acknowledgement | ☐ Drivers License | Date Issued: | Expiration Date: |
| ☐ Other _____ | ☐ Other _____ | | |

| Document Type | Date/Time Notarized: | Document Date: | Fee Charged: |
|---|---|---|---|

| Printed Name and Address of Witness: | Phone number: |
|---|---|
| | Email: |
| | Signer's Signature: |

| Comments | Record Number |
|---|---|

# NOTARY RECORD

| Printed Name and Address of Signer: | Phone number: | Thumb Print: |
|---|---|---|
| | Email: | |
| | Signer's Signature: | |

| **Service Performed** | **Identification** | ID Number: | |
|---|---|---|---|
| ☐ Jurat | ☐ ID Card  ☐ Credible Witness | Issued By: | |
| ☐ Oath | ☐ Passport  ☐ Known Personally | | |
| ☐ Acknowledgement | ☐ Drivers License | Date Issued: | Expiration Date: |
| ☐ Other _____ | ☐ Other _____ | | |

| Document Type | Date/Time Notarized: | Document Date: | Fee Charged: |
|---|---|---|---|

| Printed Name and Address of Witness: | Phone number: |
|---|---|
| | Email: |
| | Signer's Signature: |

| Comments | Record Number |
|---|---|

# NOTARY RECORD

| Printed Name and Address of Signer: | Phone number: | Thumb Print: |
|---|---|---|
| | Email: | |
| | Signer's Signature: | |

| **Service Performed** | **Identification** | | ID Number: | |
|---|---|---|---|---|
| ☐ Jurat | ☐ ID Card | ☐ Credible Witness | Issued By: | |
| ☐ Oath | ☐ Passport | ☐ Known Personally | | |
| ☐ Acknowledgement | ☐ Drivers License | | Date Issued: | Expiration Date: |
| ☐ Other _____ | ☐ Other _____ | | | |

| Document Type | Date/Time Notarized: | Document Date: | Fee Charged: |
|---|---|---|---|

| Printed Name and Address of Witness: | Phone number: |
|---|---|
| | Email: |
| | Signer's Signature: |

| Comments | Record Number |
|---|---|

# NOTARY RECORD

| Printed Name and Address of Signer: | Phone number: | Thumb Print: |
|---|---|---|
| | Email: | |
| | Signer's Signature: | |

| **Service Performed** | **Identification** | | ID Number: | |
|---|---|---|---|---|
| ☐ Jurat | ☐ ID Card | ☐ Credible Witness | Issued By: | |
| ☐ Oath | ☐ Passport | ☐ Known Personally | | |
| ☐ Acknowledgement | ☐ Drivers License | | Date Issued: | Expiration Date: |
| ☐ Other _____ | ☐ Other _____ | | | |

| Document Type | Date/Time Notarized: | Document Date: | Fee Charged: |
|---|---|---|---|

| Printed Name and Address of Witness: | Phone number: |
|---|---|
| | Email: |
| | Signer's Signature: |

| Comments | Record Number |
|---|---|

# NOTARY RECORD

| Printed Name and Address of Signer: | Phone number: | Thumb Print: |
|---|---|---|
| | Email: | |
| | Signer's Signature: | |

| **Service Performed** | **Identification** | | ID Number: | |
|---|---|---|---|---|
| ☐ Jurat | ☐ ID Card | ☐ Credible Witness | | |
| ☐ Oath | ☐ Passport | ☐ Known Personally | Issued By: | |
| ☐ Acknowledgement | ☐ Drivers License | | | |
| ☐ Other _____ | ☐ Other _____ | | Date Issued: | Expiration Date: |

| Document Type | Date/Time Notarized: | Document Date: | Fee Charged: |
|---|---|---|---|

| Printed Name and Address of Witness: | Phone number: |
|---|---|
| | Email: |
| | Signer's Signature: |

| Comments | Record Number |
|---|---|

# NOTARY RECORD

| Printed Name and Address of Signer: | Phone number: | Thumb Print: |
|---|---|---|
| | Email: | |
| | Signer's Signature: | |

| **Service Performed** | **Identification** | | ID Number: | |
|---|---|---|---|---|
| ☐ Jurat | ☐ ID Card | ☐ Credible Witness | | |
| ☐ Oath | ☐ Passport | ☐ Known Personally | Issued By: | |
| ☐ Acknowledgement | ☐ Drivers License | | | |
| ☐ Other _____ | ☐ Other _____ | | Date Issued: | Expiration Date: |

| Document Type | Date/Time Notarized: | Document Date: | Fee Charged: |
|---|---|---|---|

| Printed Name and Address of Witness: | Phone number: |
|---|---|
| | Email: |
| | Signer's Signature: |

| Comments | Record Number |
|---|---|

# NOTARY RECORD

| Printed Name and Address of Signer: | Phone number: | Thumb Print: |
|---|---|---|
| | Email: | |
| | Signer's Signature: | |

| Service Performed | Identification | | ID Number: | |
|---|---|---|---|---|
| ☐ Jurat | ☐ ID Card | ☐ Credible Witness | Issued By: | |
| ☐ Oath | ☐ Passport | ☐ Known Personally | | |
| ☐ Acknowledgement | ☐ Drivers License | | Date Issued: | Expiration Date: |
| ☐ Other _____ | ☐ Other _____ | | | |

| Document Type | Date/Time Notarized: | Document Date: | Fee Charged: |
|---|---|---|---|

| Printed Name and Address of Witness: | Phone number: |
|---|---|
| | Email: |
| | Signer's Signature: |

| Comments | Record Number |
|---|---|

# NOTARY RECORD

| Printed Name and Address of Signer: | Phone number: | Thumb Print: |
|---|---|---|
| | Email: | |
| | Signer's Signature: | |

| Service Performed | Identification | | ID Number: | |
|---|---|---|---|---|
| ☐ Jurat | ☐ ID Card | ☐ Credible Witness | Issued By: | |
| ☐ Oath | ☐ Passport | ☐ Known Personally | | |
| ☐ Acknowledgement | ☐ Drivers License | | Date Issued: | Expiration Date: |
| ☐ Other _____ | ☐ Other _____ | | | |

| Document Type | Date/Time Notarized: | Document Date: | Fee Charged: |
|---|---|---|---|

| Printed Name and Address of Witness: | Phone number: |
|---|---|
| | Email: |
| | Signer's Signature: |

| Comments | Record Number |
|---|---|

# NOTARY RECORD

| Printed Name and Address of Signer: | Phone number: | Thumb Print: |
|---|---|---|
| | Email: | |
| | Signer's Signature: | |

| **Service Performed** | **Identification** | | ID Number: | |
|---|---|---|---|---|
| ☐ Jurat | ☐ ID Card | ☐ Credible Witness | Issued By: | |
| ☐ Oath | ☐ Passport | ☐ Known Personally | | |
| ☐ Acknowledgement | ☐ Drivers License | | Date Issued: | Expiration Date: |
| ☐ Other _____ | ☐ Other _____ | | | |

| Document Type | Date/Time Notarized: | Document Date: | Fee Charged: |
|---|---|---|---|

| Printed Name and Address of Witness: | Phone number: |
|---|---|
| | Email: |
| | Signer's Signature: |

| Comments | Record Number |
|---|---|

# NOTARY RECORD

| Printed Name and Address of Signer: | Phone number: | Thumb Print: |
|---|---|---|
| | Email: | |
| | Signer's Signature: | |

| **Service Performed** | **Identification** | | ID Number: | |
|---|---|---|---|---|
| ☐ Jurat | ☐ ID Card | ☐ Credible Witness | Issued By: | |
| ☐ Oath | ☐ Passport | ☐ Known Personally | | |
| ☐ Acknowledgement | ☐ Drivers License | | Date Issued: | Expiration Date: |
| ☐ Other _____ | ☐ Other _____ | | | |

| Document Type | Date/Time Notarized: | Document Date: | Fee Charged: |
|---|---|---|---|

| Printed Name and Address of Witness: | Phone number: |
|---|---|
| | Email: |
| | Signer's Signature: |

| Comments | Record Number |
|---|---|

# NOTARY RECORD

**Printed Name and Address of Signer:**

Phone number:

Email:

Signer's Signature:

Thumb Print:

| **Service Performed** | **Identification** | | ID Number: | |
|---|---|---|---|---|
| ☐ Jurat | ☐ ID Card | ☐ Credible Witness | Issued By: | |
| ☐ Oath | ☐ Passport | ☐ Known Personally | | |
| ☐ Acknowledgement | ☐ Drivers License | | Date Issued: | Expiration Date: |
| ☐ Other _____ | ☐ Other _____ | | | |

| Document Type | Date/Time Notarized: | Document Date: | Fee Charged: |
|---|---|---|---|

**Printed Name and Address of Witness:**

Phone number:

Email:

Signer's Signature:

| Comments | Record Number |
|---|---|

---

# NOTARY RECORD

**Printed Name and Address of Signer:**

Phone number:

Email:

Signer's Signature:

Thumb Print:

| **Service Performed** | **Identification** | | ID Number: | |
|---|---|---|---|---|
| ☐ Jurat | ☐ ID Card | ☐ Credible Witness | Issued By: | |
| ☐ Oath | ☐ Passport | ☐ Known Personally | | |
| ☐ Acknowledgement | ☐ Drivers License | | Date Issued: | Expiration Date: |
| ☐ Other _____ | ☐ Other _____ | | | |

| Document Type | Date/Time Notarized: | Document Date: | Fee Charged: |
|---|---|---|---|

**Printed Name and Address of Witness:**

Phone number:

Email:

Signer's Signature:

| Comments | Record Number |
|---|---|

# NOTARY RECORD

| Printed Name and Address of Signer: | Phone number: | Thumb Print: |
|---|---|---|
| | Email: | |
| | Signer's Signature: | |

| Service Performed | Identification | ID Number: | |
|---|---|---|---|
| ☐ Jurat | ☐ ID Card  ☐ Credible Witness | Issued By: | |
| ☐ Oath | ☐ Passport  ☐ Known Personally | | |
| ☐ Acknowledgement | ☐ Drivers License | Date Issued: | Expiration Date: |
| ☐ Other _____ | ☐ Other _____ | | |

| Document Type | Date/Time Notarized: | Document Date: | Fee Charged: |
|---|---|---|---|

| Printed Name and Address of Witness: | Phone number: |
|---|---|
| | Email: |
| | Signer's Signature: |

| Comments | Record Number |
|---|---|

# NOTARY RECORD

| Printed Name and Address of Signer: | Phone number: | Thumb Print: |
|---|---|---|
| | Email: | |
| | Signer's Signature: | |

| Service Performed | Identification | ID Number: | |
|---|---|---|---|
| ☐ Jurat | ☐ ID Card  ☐ Credible Witness | Issued By: | |
| ☐ Oath | ☐ Passport  ☐ Known Personally | | |
| ☐ Acknowledgement | ☐ Drivers License | Date Issued: | Expiration Date: |
| ☐ Other _____ | ☐ Other _____ | | |

| Document Type | Date/Time Notarized: | Document Date: | Fee Charged: |
|---|---|---|---|

| Printed Name and Address of Witness: | Phone number: |
|---|---|
| | Email: |
| | Signer's Signature: |

| Comments | Record Number |
|---|---|

# NOTARY RECORD

**Printed Name and Address of Signer:**

| Phone number: | Thumb Print: |
|---|---|
| Email: | |
| Signer's Signature: | |

| **Service Performed** | **Identification** | ID Number: | |
|---|---|---|---|
| ☐ Jurat | ☐ ID Card  ☐ Credible Witness | Issued By: | |
| ☐ Oath | ☐ Passport  ☐ Known Personally | | |
| ☐ Acknowledgement | ☐ Drivers License | Date Issued: | Expiration Date: |
| ☐ Other _____ | ☐ Other _____ | | |

| Document Type | Date/Time Notarized: | Document Date: | Fee Charged: |
|---|---|---|---|

**Printed Name and Address of Witness:**

| Phone number: |
|---|
| Email: |
| Signer's Signature: |

| Comments | Record Number |
|---|---|

---

# NOTARY RECORD

**Printed Name and Address of Signer:**

| Phone number: | Thumb Print: |
|---|---|
| Email: | |
| Signer's Signature: | |

| **Service Performed** | **Identification** | ID Number: | |
|---|---|---|---|
| ☐ Jurat | ☐ ID Card  ☐ Credible Witness | Issued By: | |
| ☐ Oath | ☐ Passport  ☐ Known Personally | | |
| ☐ Acknowledgement | ☐ Drivers License | Date Issued: | Expiration Date: |
| ☐ Other _____ | ☐ Other _____ | | |

| Document Type | Date/Time Notarized: | Document Date: | Fee Charged: |
|---|---|---|---|

**Printed Name and Address of Witness:**

| Phone number: |
|---|
| Email: |
| Signer's Signature: |

| Comments | Record Number |
|---|---|

# NOTARY RECORD

| Printed Name and Address of Signer: | Phone number: | Thumb Print: |
|---|---|---|
| | Email: | |
| | Signer's Signature: | |

| **Service Performed** | **Identification** | ID Number: | |
|---|---|---|---|
| ☐ Jurat | ☐ ID Card   ☐ Credible Witness | Issued By: | |
| ☐ Oath | ☐ Passport   ☐ Known Personally | | |
| ☐ Acknowledgement | ☐ Drivers License | Date Issued: | Expiration Date: |
| ☐ Other _____ | ☐ Other _____ | | |

| Document Type | Date/Time Notarized: | Document Date: | Fee Charged: |
|---|---|---|---|

| Printed Name and Address of Witness: | Phone number: |
|---|---|
| | Email: |
| | Signer's Signature: |

| Comments | Record Number |
|---|---|

---

# NOTARY RECORD

| Printed Name and Address of Signer: | Phone number: | Thumb Print: |
|---|---|---|
| | Email: | |
| | Signer's Signature: | |

| **Service Performed** | **Identification** | ID Number: | |
|---|---|---|---|
| ☐ Jurat | ☐ ID Card   ☐ Credible Witness | Issued By: | |
| ☐ Oath | ☐ Passport   ☐ Known Personally | | |
| ☐ Acknowledgement | ☐ Drivers License | Date Issued: | Expiration Date: |
| ☐ Other _____ | ☐ Other _____ | | |

| Document Type | Date/Time Notarized: | Document Date: | Fee Charged: |
|---|---|---|---|

| Printed Name and Address of Witness: | Phone number: |
|---|---|
| | Email: |
| | Signer's Signature: |

| Comments | Record Number |
|---|---|

# NOTARY RECORD

| Printed Name and Address of Signer: | Phone number: | Thumb Print: |
|---|---|---|
| | Email: | |
| | Signer's Signature: | |

| **Service Performed** | **Identification** | | ID Number: | |
|---|---|---|---|---|
| ☐ Jurat | ☐ ID Card | ☐ Credible Witness | Issued By: | |
| ☐ Oath | ☐ Passport | ☐ Known Personally | | |
| ☐ Acknowledgement | ☐ Drivers License | | Date Issued: | Expiration Date: |
| ☐ Other _____ | ☐ Other _____ | | | |

| Document Type | Date/Time Notarized: | Document Date: | Fee Charged: |
|---|---|---|---|

| Printed Name and Address of Witness: | Phone number: |
|---|---|
| | Email: |
| | Signer's Signature: |

| Comments | Record Number |
|---|---|

# NOTARY RECORD

| Printed Name and Address of Signer: | Phone number: | Thumb Print: |
|---|---|---|
| | Email: | |
| | Signer's Signature: | |

| **Service Performed** | **Identification** | | ID Number: | |
|---|---|---|---|---|
| ☐ Jurat | ☐ ID Card | ☐ Credible Witness | Issued By: | |
| ☐ Oath | ☐ Passport | ☐ Known Personally | | |
| ☐ Acknowledgement | ☐ Drivers License | | Date Issued: | Expiration Date: |
| ☐ Other _____ | ☐ Other _____ | | | |

| Document Type | Date/Time Notarized: | Document Date: | Fee Charged: |
|---|---|---|---|

| Printed Name and Address of Witness: | Phone number: |
|---|---|
| | Email: |
| | Signer's Signature: |

| Comments | Record Number |
|---|---|

# NOTARY RECORD

| Printed Name and Address of Signer: | Phone number: | Thumb Print: |
|---|---|---|
| | Email: | |
| | Signer's Signature: | |

| **Service Performed** | **Identification** | ID Number: | |
|---|---|---|---|
| ☐ Jurat | ☐ ID Card ☐ Credible Witness | Issued By: | |
| ☐ Oath | ☐ Passport ☐ Known Personally | | |
| ☐ Acknowledgement | ☐ Drivers License | Date Issued: | Expiration Date: |
| ☐ Other _____ | ☐ Other _____ | | |

| Document Type | Date/Time Notarized: | Document Date: | Fee Charged: |
|---|---|---|---|

| Printed Name and Address of Witness: | Phone number: |
|---|---|
| | Email: |
| | Signer's Signature: |

| Comments | Record Number |
|---|---|

---

# NOTARY RECORD

| Printed Name and Address of Signer: | Phone number: | Thumb Print: |
|---|---|---|
| | Email: | |
| | Signer's Signature: | |

| **Service Performed** | **Identification** | ID Number: | |
|---|---|---|---|
| ☐ Jurat | ☐ ID Card ☐ Credible Witness | Issued By: | |
| ☐ Oath | ☐ Passport ☐ Known Personally | | |
| ☐ Acknowledgement | ☐ Drivers License | Date Issued: | Expiration Date: |
| ☐ Other _____ | ☐ Other _____ | | |

| Document Type | Date/Time Notarized: | Document Date: | Fee Charged: |
|---|---|---|---|

| Printed Name and Address of Witness: | Phone number: |
|---|---|
| | Email: |
| | Signer's Signature: |

| Comments | Record Number |
|---|---|

# NOTARY RECORD

**Printed Name and Address of Signer:**

Phone number:

Email:

Signer's Signature:

Thumb Print:

| Service Performed | Identification | | ID Number: | |
|---|---|---|---|---|
| ☐ Jurat | ☐ ID Card | ☐ Credible Witness | | |
| ☐ Oath | ☐ Passport | ☐ Known Personally | Issued By: | |
| ☐ Acknowledgement | ☐ Drivers License | | | |
| ☐ Other _____ | ☐ Other _____ | | Date Issued: | Expiration Date: |

| Document Type | Date/Time Notarized: | Document Date: | Fee Charged: |
|---|---|---|---|

**Printed Name and Address of Witness:**

Phone number:

Email:

Signer's Signature:

| Comments | Record Number |
|---|---|

---

# NOTARY RECORD

**Printed Name and Address of Signer:**

Phone number:

Email:

Signer's Signature:

Thumb Print:

| Service Performed | Identification | | ID Number: | |
|---|---|---|---|---|
| ☐ Jurat | ☐ ID Card | ☐ Credible Witness | | |
| ☐ Oath | ☐ Passport | ☐ Known Personally | Issued By: | |
| ☐ Acknowledgement | ☐ Drivers License | | | |
| ☐ Other _____ | ☐ Other _____ | | Date Issued: | Expiration Date: |

| Document Type | Date/Time Notarized: | Document Date: | Fee Charged: |
|---|---|---|---|

**Printed Name and Address of Witness:**

Phone number:

Email:

Signer's Signature:

| Comments | Record Number |
|---|---|

# NOTARY RECORD

| Printed Name and Address of Signer: | Phone number: | Thumb Print: |
|---|---|---|
| | Email: | |
| | Signer's Signature: | |

| **Service Performed** | **Identification** | | ID Number: | |
|---|---|---|---|---|
| ☐ Jurat | ☐ ID Card | ☐ Credible Witness | Issued By: | |
| ☐ Oath | ☐ Passport | ☐ Known Personally | | |
| ☐ Acknowledgement | ☐ Drivers License | | Date Issued: | Expiration Date: |
| ☐ Other _____ | ☐ Other _____ | | | |
| Document Type | Date/Time Notarized: | | Document Date: | Fee Charged: |

| Printed Name and Address of Witness: | Phone number: |
|---|---|
| | Email: |
| | Signer's Signature: |

| Comments | Record Number |
|---|---|

# NOTARY RECORD

| Printed Name and Address of Signer: | Phone number: | Thumb Print: |
|---|---|---|
| | Email: | |
| | Signer's Signature: | |

| **Service Performed** | **Identification** | | ID Number: | |
|---|---|---|---|---|
| ☐ Jurat | ☐ ID Card | ☐ Credible Witness | Issued By: | |
| ☐ Oath | ☐ Passport | ☐ Known Personally | | |
| ☐ Acknowledgement | ☐ Drivers License | | Date Issued: | Expiration Date: |
| ☐ Other _____ | ☐ Other _____ | | | |
| Document Type | Date/Time Notarized: | | Document Date: | Fee Charged: |

| Printed Name and Address of Witness: | Phone number: |
|---|---|
| | Email: |
| | Signer's Signature: |

| Comments | Record Number |
|---|---|

# NOTARY RECORD

| Printed Name and Address of Signer: | Phone number: | Thumb Print: |
|---|---|---|
| | Email: | |
| | Signer's Signature: | |

| Service Performed | Identification | | ID Number: | |
|---|---|---|---|---|
| ☐ Jurat | ☐ ID Card | ☐ Credible Witness | Issued By: | |
| ☐ Oath | ☐ Passport | ☐ Known Personally | | |
| ☐ Acknowledgement | ☐ Drivers License | | Date Issued: | Expiration Date: |
| ☐ Other _____ | ☐ Other _____ | | | |

| Document Type | Date/Time Notarized: | Document Date: | Fee Charged: |
|---|---|---|---|

| Printed Name and Address of Witness: | Phone number: |
|---|---|
| | Email: |
| | Signer's Signature: |

| Comments | Record Number |
|---|---|

# NOTARY RECORD

| Printed Name and Address of Signer: | Phone number: | Thumb Print: |
|---|---|---|
| | Email: | |
| | Signer's Signature: | |

| Service Performed | Identification | | ID Number: | |
|---|---|---|---|---|
| ☐ Jurat | ☐ ID Card | ☐ Credible Witness | Issued By: | |
| ☐ Oath | ☐ Passport | ☐ Known Personally | | |
| ☐ Acknowledgement | ☐ Drivers License | | Date Issued: | Expiration Date: |
| ☐ Other _____ | ☐ Other _____ | | | |

| Document Type | Date/Time Notarized: | Document Date: | Fee Charged: |
|---|---|---|---|

| Printed Name and Address of Witness: | Phone number: |
|---|---|
| | Email: |
| | Signer's Signature: |

| Comments | Record Number |
|---|---|

# NOTARY RECORD

| Printed Name and Address of Signer: | Phone number: | Thumb Print: |
|---|---|---|
| | Email: | |
| | Signer's Signature: | |

| **Service Performed** | **Identification** | | ID Number: | |
|---|---|---|---|---|
| ☐ Jurat | ☐ ID Card | ☐ Credible Witness | | |
| ☐ Oath | ☐ Passport | ☐ Known Personally | Issued By: | |
| ☐ Acknowledgement | ☐ Drivers License | | Date Issued: | Expiration Date: |
| ☐ Other _____ | ☐ Other _____ | | | |

| Document Type | Date/Time Notarized: | Document Date: | Fee Charged: |
|---|---|---|---|

| Printed Name and Address of Witness: | Phone number: |
|---|---|
| | Email: |
| | Signer's Signature: |

| Comments | Record Number |
|---|---|

# NOTARY RECORD

| Printed Name and Address of Signer: | Phone number: | Thumb Print: |
|---|---|---|
| | Email: | |
| | Signer's Signature: | |

| **Service Performed** | **Identification** | | ID Number: | |
|---|---|---|---|---|
| ☐ Jurat | ☐ ID Card | ☐ Credible Witness | | |
| ☐ Oath | ☐ Passport | ☐ Known Personally | Issued By: | |
| ☐ Acknowledgement | ☐ Drivers License | | Date Issued: | Expiration Date: |
| ☐ Other _____ | ☐ Other _____ | | | |

| Document Type | Date/Time Notarized: | Document Date: | Fee Charged: |
|---|---|---|---|

| Printed Name and Address of Witness: | Phone number: |
|---|---|
| | Email: |
| | Signer's Signature: |

| Comments | Record Number |
|---|---|

# NOTARY RECORD

| Printed Name and Address of Signer: | Phone number: | Thumb Print: |
| --- | --- | --- |
| | Email: | |
| | Signer's Signature: | |

| **Service Performed** | **Identification** | ID Number: | |
| --- | --- | --- | --- |
| ☐ Jurat | ☐ ID Card    ☐ Credible Witness | Issued By: | |
| ☐ Oath | ☐ Passport   ☐ Known Personally | | |
| ☐ Acknowledgement | ☐ Drivers License | Date Issued: | Expiration Date: |
| ☐ Other _____ | ☐ Other _____ | | |

| Document Type | Date/Time Notarized: | Document Date: | Fee Charged: |
| --- | --- | --- | --- |

| Printed Name and Address of Witness: | Phone number: |
| --- | --- |
| | Email: |
| | Signer's Signature: |

| Comments | Record Number |
| --- | --- |

# NOTARY RECORD

| Printed Name and Address of Signer: | Phone number: | Thumb Print: |
| --- | --- | --- |
| | Email: | |
| | Signer's Signature: | |

| **Service Performed** | **Identification** | ID Number: | |
| --- | --- | --- | --- |
| ☐ Jurat | ☐ ID Card    ☐ Credible Witness | Issued By: | |
| ☐ Oath | ☐ Passport   ☐ Known Personally | | |
| ☐ Acknowledgement | ☐ Drivers License | Date Issued: | Expiration Date: |
| ☐ Other _____ | ☐ Other _____ | | |

| Document Type | Date/Time Notarized: | Document Date: | Fee Charged: |
| --- | --- | --- | --- |

| Printed Name and Address of Witness: | Phone number: |
| --- | --- |
| | Email: |
| | Signer's Signature: |

| Comments | Record Number |
| --- | --- |

# NOTARY RECORD

| Printed Name and Address of Signer: | Phone number: | Thumb Print: |
|---|---|---|
| | Email: | |
| | Signer's Signature: | |

| **Service Performed** | **Identification** | | ID Number: | |
|---|---|---|---|---|
| ☐ Jurat | ☐ ID Card | ☐ Credible Witness | | |
| ☐ Oath | ☐ Passport | ☐ Known Personally | Issued By: | |
| ☐ Acknowledgement | ☐ Drivers License | | Date Issued: | Expiration Date: |
| ☐ Other _____ | ☐ Other _____ | | | |

| Document Type | Date/Time Notarized: | Document Date: | Fee Charged: |
|---|---|---|---|

| Printed Name and Address of Witness: | Phone number: |
|---|---|
| | Email: |
| | Signer's Signature: |

| Comments | Record Number |
|---|---|

# NOTARY RECORD

| Printed Name and Address of Signer: | Phone number: | Thumb Print: |
|---|---|---|
| | Email: | |
| | Signer's Signature: | |

| **Service Performed** | **Identification** | | ID Number: | |
|---|---|---|---|---|
| ☐ Jurat | ☐ ID Card | ☐ Credible Witness | | |
| ☐ Oath | ☐ Passport | ☐ Known Personally | Issued By: | |
| ☐ Acknowledgement | ☐ Drivers License | | Date Issued: | Expiration Date: |
| ☐ Other _____ | ☐ Other _____ | | | |

| Document Type | Date/Time Notarized: | Document Date: | Fee Charged: |
|---|---|---|---|

| Printed Name and Address of Witness: | Phone number: |
|---|---|
| | Email: |
| | Signer's Signature: |

| Comments | Record Number |
|---|---|

# NOTARY RECORD

| Printed Name and Address of Signer: | Phone number: | Thumb Print: |
|---|---|---|
| | Email: | |
| | Signer's Signature: | |

| Service Performed | Identification | ID Number: | |
|---|---|---|---|
| ☐ Jurat | ☐ ID Card   ☐ Credible Witness | Issued By: | |
| ☐ Oath | ☐ Passport   ☐ Known Personally | | |
| ☐ Acknowledgement | ☐ Drivers License | Date Issued: | Expiration Date: |
| ☐ Other _____ | ☐ Other _____ | | |

| Document Type | Date/Time Notarized: | Document Date: | Fee Charged: |
|---|---|---|---|

| Printed Name and Address of Witness: | Phone number: |
|---|---|
| | Email: |
| | Signer's Signature: |

| Comments | Record Number |
|---|---|

# NOTARY RECORD

| Printed Name and Address of Signer: | Phone number: | Thumb Print: |
|---|---|---|
| | Email: | |
| | Signer's Signature: | |

| Service Performed | Identification | ID Number: | |
|---|---|---|---|
| ☐ Jurat | ☐ ID Card   ☐ Credible Witness | Issued By: | |
| ☐ Oath | ☐ Passport   ☐ Known Personally | | |
| ☐ Acknowledgement | ☐ Drivers License | Date Issued: | Expiration Date: |
| ☐ Other _____ | ☐ Other _____ | | |

| Document Type | Date/Time Notarized: | Document Date: | Fee Charged: |
|---|---|---|---|

| Printed Name and Address of Witness: | Phone number: |
|---|---|
| | Email: |
| | Signer's Signature: |

| Comments | Record Number |
|---|---|

# NOTARY RECORD

| Printed Name and Address of Signer: | Phone number: | Thumb Print: |
|---|---|---|
| | Email: | |
| | Signer's Signature: | |

| **Service Performed** | **Identification** | | ID Number: | |
|---|---|---|---|---|
| ☐ Jurat | ☐ ID Card | ☐ Credible Witness | Issued By: | |
| ☐ Oath | ☐ Passport | ☐ Known Personally | | |
| ☐ Acknowledgement | ☐ Drivers License | | Date Issued: | Expiration Date: |
| ☐ Other _____ | ☐ Other _____ | | | |

| Document Type | Date/Time Notarized: | Document Date: | Fee Charged: |
|---|---|---|---|

| Printed Name and Address of Witness: | Phone number: |
|---|---|
| | Email: |
| | Signer's Signature: |

| Comments | Record Number |
|---|---|

# NOTARY RECORD

| Printed Name and Address of Signer: | Phone number: | Thumb Print: |
|---|---|---|
| | Email: | |
| | Signer's Signature: | |

| **Service Performed** | **Identification** | | ID Number: | |
|---|---|---|---|---|
| ☐ Jurat | ☐ ID Card | ☐ Credible Witness | Issued By: | |
| ☐ Oath | ☐ Passport | ☐ Known Personally | | |
| ☐ Acknowledgement | ☐ Drivers License | | Date Issued: | Expiration Date: |
| ☐ Other _____ | ☐ Other _____ | | | |

| Document Type | Date/Time Notarized: | Document Date: | Fee Charged: |
|---|---|---|---|

| Printed Name and Address of Witness: | Phone number: |
|---|---|
| | Email: |
| | Signer's Signature: |

| Comments | Record Number |
|---|---|

# NOTARY RECORD

| Printed Name and Address of Signer: | Phone number: | Thumb Print: |
|---|---|---|
| | Email: | |
| | Signer's Signature: | |

| **Service Performed** | **Identification** | ID Number: | |
|---|---|---|---|
| ☐ Jurat | ☐ ID Card  ☐ Credible Witness | Issued By: | |
| ☐ Oath | ☐ Passport  ☐ Known Personally | | |
| ☐ Acknowledgement | ☐ Drivers License | Date Issued: | Expiration Date: |
| ☐ Other _____ | ☐ Other _____ | | |

| Document Type | Date/Time Notarized: | Document Date: | Fee Charged: |
|---|---|---|---|

| Printed Name and Address of Witness: | Phone number: |
|---|---|
| | Email: |
| | Signer's Signature: |

| Comments | Record Number |
|---|---|

# NOTARY RECORD

| Printed Name and Address of Signer: | Phone number: | Thumb Print: |
|---|---|---|
| | Email: | |
| | Signer's Signature: | |

| **Service Performed** | **Identification** | ID Number: | |
|---|---|---|---|
| ☐ Jurat | ☐ ID Card  ☐ Credible Witness | Issued By: | |
| ☐ Oath | ☐ Passport  ☐ Known Personally | | |
| ☐ Acknowledgement | ☐ Drivers License | Date Issued: | Expiration Date: |
| ☐ Other _____ | ☐ Other _____ | | |

| Document Type | Date/Time Notarized: | Document Date: | Fee Charged: |
|---|---|---|---|

| Printed Name and Address of Witness: | Phone number: |
|---|---|
| | Email: |
| | Signer's Signature: |

| Comments | Record Number |
|---|---|

# NOTARY RECORD

**Printed Name and Address of Signer:**

Phone number:

Email:

Signer's Signature:

Thumb Print:

| **Service Performed** | **Identification** | | ID Number: | |
|---|---|---|---|---|
| ☐ Jurat | ☐ ID Card | ☐ Credible Witness | Issued By: | |
| ☐ Oath | ☐ Passport | ☐ Known Personally | | |
| ☐ Acknowledgement | ☐ Drivers License | | Date Issued: | Expiration Date: |
| ☐ Other _____ | ☐ Other _____ | | | |

| Document Type | Date/Time Notarized: | Document Date: | Fee Charged: |
|---|---|---|---|

**Printed Name and Address of Witness:**

Phone number:

Email:

Signer's Signature:

| Comments | Record Number |
|---|---|

# NOTARY RECORD

**Printed Name and Address of Signer:**

Phone number:

Email:

Signer's Signature:

Thumb Print:

| **Service Performed** | **Identification** | | ID Number: | |
|---|---|---|---|---|
| ☐ Jurat | ☐ ID Card | ☐ Credible Witness | Issued By: | |
| ☐ Oath | ☐ Passport | ☐ Known Personally | | |
| ☐ Acknowledgement | ☐ Drivers License | | Date Issued: | Expiration Date: |
| ☐ Other _____ | ☐ Other _____ | | | |

| Document Type | Date/Time Notarized: | Document Date: | Fee Charged: |
|---|---|---|---|

**Printed Name and Address of Witness:**

Phone number:

Email:

Signer's Signature:

| Comments | Record Number |
|---|---|

# NOTARY RECORD

| Printed Name and Address of Signer: | Phone number: | Thumb Print: |
|---|---|---|
| | Email: | |
| | Signer's Signature: | |

| **Service Performed** | **Identification** | | ID Number: | |
|---|---|---|---|---|
| ☐ Jurat | ☐ ID Card | ☐ Credible Witness | Issued By: | |
| ☐ Oath | ☐ Passport | ☐ Known Personally | | |
| ☐ Acknowledgement | ☐ Drivers License | | Date Issued: | Expiration Date: |
| ☐ Other _____ | ☐ Other _____ | | | |

| Document Type | Date/Time Notarized: | Document Date: | Fee Charged: |
|---|---|---|---|

| Printed Name and Address of Witness: | Phone number: |
|---|---|
| | Email: |
| | Signer's Signature: |

| Comments | Record Number |
|---|---|

# NOTARY RECORD

| Printed Name and Address of Signer: | Phone number: | Thumb Print: |
|---|---|---|
| | Email: | |
| | Signer's Signature: | |

| **Service Performed** | **Identification** | | ID Number: | |
|---|---|---|---|---|
| ☐ Jurat | ☐ ID Card | ☐ Credible Witness | Issued By: | |
| ☐ Oath | ☐ Passport | ☐ Known Personally | | |
| ☐ Acknowledgement | ☐ Drivers License | | Date Issued: | Expiration Date: |
| ☐ Other _____ | ☐ Other _____ | | | |

| Document Type | Date/Time Notarized: | Document Date: | Fee Charged: |
|---|---|---|---|

| Printed Name and Address of Witness: | Phone number: |
|---|---|
| | Email: |
| | Signer's Signature: |

| Comments | Record Number |
|---|---|

# NOTARY RECORD

| Printed Name and Address of Signer: | Phone number: | Thumb Print: |
|---|---|---|
| | Email: | |
| | Signer's Signature: | |

| **Service Performed** | **Identification** | ID Number: | |
|---|---|---|---|
| ☐ Jurat | ☐ ID Card ☐ Credible Witness | Issued By: | |
| ☐ Oath | ☐ Passport ☐ Known Personally | | |
| ☐ Acknowledgement | ☐ Drivers License | Date Issued: | Expiration Date: |
| ☐ Other _____ | ☐ Other _____ | | |

| Document Type | Date/Time Notarized: | Document Date: | Fee Charged: |
|---|---|---|---|

| Printed Name and Address of Witness: | Phone number: |
|---|---|
| | Email: |
| | Signer's Signature: |

| Comments | Record Number |
|---|---|

# NOTARY RECORD

| Printed Name and Address of Signer: | Phone number: | Thumb Print: |
|---|---|---|
| | Email: | |
| | Signer's Signature: | |

| **Service Performed** | **Identification** | ID Number: | |
|---|---|---|---|
| ☐ Jurat | ☐ ID Card ☐ Credible Witness | Issued By: | |
| ☐ Oath | ☐ Passport ☐ Known Personally | | |
| ☐ Acknowledgement | ☐ Drivers License | Date Issued: | Expiration Date: |
| ☐ Other _____ | ☐ Other _____ | | |

| Document Type | Date/Time Notarized: | Document Date: | Fee Charged: |
|---|---|---|---|

| Printed Name and Address of Witness: | Phone number: |
|---|---|
| | Email: |
| | Signer's Signature: |

| Comments | Record Number |
|---|---|

# NOTARY RECORD

| Printed Name and Address of Signer: | Phone number: | Thumb Print: |
|---|---|---|
| | Email: | |
| | Signer's Signature: | |

| **Service Performed** | **Identification** | ID Number: | |
|---|---|---|---|
| ☐ Jurat | ☐ ID Card   ☐ Credible Witness | Issued By: | |
| ☐ Oath | ☐ Passport   ☐ Known Personally | | |
| ☐ Acknowledgement | ☐ Drivers License | Date Issued: | Expiration Date: |
| ☐ Other _____ | ☐ Other _____ | | |

| Document Type | Date/Time Notarized: | Document Date: | Fee Charged: |
|---|---|---|---|

| Printed Name and Address of Witness: | Phone number: |
|---|---|
| | Email: |
| | Signer's Signature: |

| Comments | Record Number |
|---|---|

# NOTARY RECORD

| Printed Name and Address of Signer: | Phone number: | Thumb Print: |
|---|---|---|
| | Email: | |
| | Signer's Signature: | |

| **Service Performed** | **Identification** | ID Number: | |
|---|---|---|---|
| ☐ Jurat | ☐ ID Card   ☐ Credible Witness | Issued By: | |
| ☐ Oath | ☐ Passport   ☐ Known Personally | | |
| ☐ Acknowledgement | ☐ Drivers License | Date Issued: | Expiration Date: |
| ☐ Other _____ | ☐ Other _____ | | |

| Document Type | Date/Time Notarized: | Document Date: | Fee Charged: |
|---|---|---|---|

| Printed Name and Address of Witness: | Phone number: |
|---|---|
| | Email: |
| | Signer's Signature: |

| Comments | Record Number |
|---|---|

# NOTARY RECORD

| Printed Name and Address of Signer: | Phone number: | Thumb Print: |
|---|---|---|
| | Email: | |
| | Signer's Signature: | |

| Service Performed | Identification | ID Number: | |
|---|---|---|---|
| ☐ Jurat | ☐ ID Card  ☐ Credible Witness | Issued By: | |
| ☐ Oath | ☐ Passport  ☐ Known Personally | | |
| ☐ Acknowledgement | ☐ Drivers License | Date Issued: | Expiration Date: |
| ☐ Other _____ | ☐ Other _____ | | |

| Document Type | Date/Time Notarized: | Document Date: | Fee Charged: |
|---|---|---|---|

| Printed Name and Address of Witness: | Phone number: |
|---|---|
| | Email: |
| | Signer's Signature: |

| Comments | Record Number |
|---|---|

---

# NOTARY RECORD

| Printed Name and Address of Signer: | Phone number: | Thumb Print: |
|---|---|---|
| | Email: | |
| | Signer's Signature: | |

| Service Performed | Identification | ID Number: | |
|---|---|---|---|
| ☐ Jurat | ☐ ID Card  ☐ Credible Witness | Issued By: | |
| ☐ Oath | ☐ Passport  ☐ Known Personally | | |
| ☐ Acknowledgement | ☐ Drivers License | Date Issued: | Expiration Date: |
| ☐ Other _____ | ☐ Other _____ | | |

| Document Type | Date/Time Notarized: | Document Date: | Fee Charged: |
|---|---|---|---|

| Printed Name and Address of Witness: | Phone number: |
|---|---|
| | Email: |
| | Signer's Signature: |

| Comments | Record Number |
|---|---|

# NOTARY RECORD

| Printed Name and Address of Signer: | Phone number: | Thumb Print: |
|---|---|---|
| | Email: | |
| | Signer's Signature: | |

| **Service Performed** | **Identification** | ID Number: | |
|---|---|---|---|
| ☐ Jurat | ☐ ID Card  ☐ Credible Witness | Issued By: | |
| ☐ Oath | ☐ Passport  ☐ Known Personally | | |
| ☐ Acknowledgement | ☐ Drivers License | Date Issued: | Expiration Date: |
| ☐ Other _____ | ☐ Other _____ | | |

| Document Type | Date/Time Notarized: | Document Date: | Fee Charged: |
|---|---|---|---|

| Printed Name and Address of Witness: | Phone number: |
|---|---|
| | Email: |
| | Signer's Signature: |

| Comments | Record Number |
|---|---|

---

# NOTARY RECORD

| Printed Name and Address of Signer: | Phone number: | Thumb Print: |
|---|---|---|
| | Email: | |
| | Signer's Signature: | |

| **Service Performed** | **Identification** | ID Number: | |
|---|---|---|---|
| ☐ Jurat | ☐ ID Card  ☐ Credible Witness | Issued By: | |
| ☐ Oath | ☐ Passport  ☐ Known Personally | | |
| ☐ Acknowledgement | ☐ Drivers License | Date Issued: | Expiration Date: |
| ☐ Other _____ | ☐ Other _____ | | |

| Document Type | Date/Time Notarized: | Document Date: | Fee Charged: |
|---|---|---|---|

| Printed Name and Address of Witness: | Phone number: |
|---|---|
| | Email: |
| | Signer's Signature: |

| Comments | Record Number |
|---|---|

# NOTARY RECORD

Printed Name and Address of Signer:

Phone number:

Email:

Signer's Signature:

Thumb Print:

| Service Performed | Identification | | ID Number: | |
|---|---|---|---|---|
| ☐ Jurat | ☐ ID Card | ☐ Credible Witness | Issued By: | |
| ☐ Oath | ☐ Passport | ☐ Known Personally | | |
| ☐ Acknowledgement | ☐ Drivers License | | Date Issued: | Expiration Date: |
| ☐ Other _____ | ☐ Other _____ | | | |

| Document Type | Date/Time Notarized: | Document Date: | Fee Charged: |
|---|---|---|---|

Printed Name and Address of Witness:

Phone number:

Email:

Signer's Signature:

Comments

Record Number

---

# NOTARY RECORD

Printed Name and Address of Signer:

Phone number:

Email:

Signer's Signature:

Thumb Print:

| Service Performed | Identification | | ID Number: | |
|---|---|---|---|---|
| ☐ Jurat | ☐ ID Card | ☐ Credible Witness | Issued By: | |
| ☐ Oath | ☐ Passport | ☐ Known Personally | | |
| ☐ Acknowledgement | ☐ Drivers License | | Date Issued: | Expiration Date: |
| ☐ Other _____ | ☐ Other _____ | | | |

| Document Type | Date/Time Notarized: | Document Date: | Fee Charged: |
|---|---|---|---|

Printed Name and Address of Witness:

Phone number:

Email:

Signer's Signature:

Comments

Record Number

# NOTARY RECORD

| Printed Name and Address of Signer: | Phone number: | Thumb Print: |
|---|---|---|
| | Email: | |
| | Signer's Signature: | |

| **Service Performed** | **Identification** | ID Number: | |
|---|---|---|---|
| ☐ Jurat | ☐ ID Card    ☐ Credible Witness | Issued By: | |
| ☐ Oath | ☐ Passport    ☐ Known Personally | | |
| ☐ Acknowledgement | ☐ Drivers License | Date Issued: | Expiration Date: |
| ☐ Other _____ | ☐ Other _____ | | |

| Document Type | Date/Time Notarized: | Document Date: | Fee Charged: |
|---|---|---|---|

| Printed Name and Address of Witness: | Phone number: |
|---|---|
| | Email: |
| | Signer's Signature: |

| Comments | Record Number |
|---|---|

# NOTARY RECORD

| Printed Name and Address of Signer: | Phone number: | Thumb Print: |
|---|---|---|
| | Email: | |
| | Signer's Signature: | |

| **Service Performed** | **Identification** | ID Number: | |
|---|---|---|---|
| ☐ Jurat | ☐ ID Card    ☐ Credible Witness | Issued By: | |
| ☐ Oath | ☐ Passport    ☐ Known Personally | | |
| ☐ Acknowledgement | ☐ Drivers License | Date Issued: | Expiration Date: |
| ☐ Other _____ | ☐ Other _____ | | |

| Document Type | Date/Time Notarized: | Document Date: | Fee Charged: |
|---|---|---|---|

| Printed Name and Address of Witness: | Phone number: |
|---|---|
| | Email: |
| | Signer's Signature: |

| Comments | Record Number |
|---|---|

# NOTARY RECORD

| Printed Name and Address of Signer: | Phone number: | Thumb Print: |
|---|---|---|
| | Email: | |
| | Signer's Signature: | |

| **Service Performed** | **Identification** | ID Number: | |
|---|---|---|---|
| ☐ Jurat | ☐ ID Card ☐ Credible Witness | Issued By: | |
| ☐ Oath | ☐ Passport ☐ Known Personally | | |
| ☐ Acknowledgement | ☐ Drivers License | Date Issued: | Expiration Date: |
| ☐ Other _____ | ☐ Other _____ | | |

| Document Type | Date/Time Notarized: | Document Date: | Fee Charged: |
|---|---|---|---|

| Printed Name and Address of Witness: | Phone number: |
|---|---|
| | Email: |
| | Signer's Signature: |

| Comments | Record Number |
|---|---|

---

# NOTARY RECORD

| Printed Name and Address of Signer: | Phone number: | Thumb Print: |
|---|---|---|
| | Email: | |
| | Signer's Signature: | |

| **Service Performed** | **Identification** | ID Number: | |
|---|---|---|---|
| ☐ Jurat | ☐ ID Card ☐ Credible Witness | Issued By: | |
| ☐ Oath | ☐ Passport ☐ Known Personally | | |
| ☐ Acknowledgement | ☐ Drivers License | Date Issued: | Expiration Date: |
| ☐ Other _____ | ☐ Other _____ | | |

| Document Type | Date/Time Notarized: | Document Date: | Fee Charged: |
|---|---|---|---|

| Printed Name and Address of Witness: | Phone number: |
|---|---|
| | Email: |
| | Signer's Signature: |

| Comments | Record Number |
|---|---|

# NOTARY RECORD

| Printed Name and Address of Signer: | Phone number: | Thumb Print: |
|---|---|---|
| | Email: | |
| | Signer's Signature: | |

**Service Performed**

☐ Jurat
☐ Oath
☐ Acknowledgement
☐ Other _____

**Identification**

☐ ID Card ☐ Credible Witness
☐ Passport ☐ Known Personally
☐ Drivers License
☐ Other _____

| ID Number: | |
|---|---|
| Issued By: | |

| Date Issued: | Expiration Date: |
|---|---|

| Document Type | Date/Time Notarized: | Document Date: | Fee Charged: |
|---|---|---|---|

| Printed Name and Address of Witness: | Phone number: |
|---|---|
| | Email: |
| | Signer's Signature: |

| Comments | Record Number |
|---|---|

# NOTARY RECORD

| Printed Name and Address of Signer: | Phone number: | Thumb Print: |
|---|---|---|
| | Email: | |
| | Signer's Signature: | |

**Service Performed**

☐ Jurat
☐ Oath
☐ Acknowledgement
☐ Other _____

**Identification**

☐ ID Card ☐ Credible Witness
☐ Passport ☐ Known Personally
☐ Drivers License
☐ Other _____

| ID Number: | |
|---|---|
| Issued By: | |

| Date Issued: | Expiration Date: |
|---|---|

| Document Type | Date/Time Notarized: | Document Date: | Fee Charged: |
|---|---|---|---|

| Printed Name and Address of Witness: | Phone number: |
|---|---|
| | Email: |
| | Signer's Signature: |

| Comments | Record Number |
|---|---|

# NOTARY RECORD

| Printed Name and Address of Signer: | Phone number: | Thumb Print: |
|---|---|---|
| | Email: | |
| | Signer's Signature: | |

| **Service Performed** | **Identification** | | ID Number: | |
|---|---|---|---|---|
| ☐ Jurat | ☐ ID Card | ☐ Credible Witness | Issued By: | |
| ☐ Oath | ☐ Passport | ☐ Known Personally | | |
| ☐ Acknowledgement | ☐ Drivers License | | Date Issued: | Expiration Date: |
| ☐ Other _____ | ☐ Other _____ | | | |
| Document Type | Date/Time Notarized: | | Document Date: | Fee Charged: |

| Printed Name and Address of Witness: | Phone number: |
|---|---|
| | Email: |
| | Signer's Signature: |

| Comments | Record Number |
|---|---|

# NOTARY RECORD

| Printed Name and Address of Signer: | Phone number: | Thumb Print: |
|---|---|---|
| | Email: | |
| | Signer's Signature: | |

| **Service Performed** | **Identification** | | ID Number: | |
|---|---|---|---|---|
| ☐ Jurat | ☐ ID Card | ☐ Credible Witness | Issued By: | |
| ☐ Oath | ☐ Passport | ☐ Known Personally | | |
| ☐ Acknowledgement | ☐ Drivers License | | Date Issued: | Expiration Date: |
| ☐ Other _____ | ☐ Other _____ | | | |
| Document Type | Date/Time Notarized: | | Document Date: | Fee Charged: |

| Printed Name and Address of Witness: | Phone number: |
|---|---|
| | Email: |
| | Signer's Signature: |

| Comments | Record Number |
|---|---|

# NOTARY RECORD

| Printed Name and Address of Signer: | Phone number: | Thumb Print: |
|---|---|---|
| | Email: | |
| | Signer's Signature: | |

| Service Performed | Identification | | ID Number: | |
|---|---|---|---|---|
| ☐ Jurat | ☐ ID Card | ☐ Credible Witness | Issued By: | |
| ☐ Oath | ☐ Passport | ☐ Known Personally | | |
| ☐ Acknowledgement | ☐ Drivers License | | Date Issued: | Expiration Date: |
| ☐ Other _____ | ☐ Other _____ | | | |

| Document Type | Date/Time Notarized: | Document Date: | Fee Charged: |
|---|---|---|---|

| Printed Name and Address of Witness: | Phone number: |
|---|---|
| | Email: |
| | Signer's Signature: |

| Comments | Record Number |
|---|---|

---

# NOTARY RECORD

| Printed Name and Address of Signer: | Phone number: | Thumb Print: |
|---|---|---|
| | Email: | |
| | Signer's Signature: | |

| Service Performed | Identification | | ID Number: | |
|---|---|---|---|---|
| ☐ Jurat | ☐ ID Card | ☐ Credible Witness | Issued By: | |
| ☐ Oath | ☐ Passport | ☐ Known Personally | | |
| ☐ Acknowledgement | ☐ Drivers License | | Date Issued: | Expiration Date: |
| ☐ Other _____ | ☐ Other _____ | | | |

| Document Type | Date/Time Notarized: | Document Date: | Fee Charged: |
|---|---|---|---|

| Printed Name and Address of Witness: | Phone number: |
|---|---|
| | Email: |
| | Signer's Signature: |

| Comments | Record Number |
|---|---|

# NOTARY RECORD

| Printed Name and Address of Signer: | Phone number: | Thumb Print: |
|---|---|---|
| | Email: | |
| | Signer's Signature: | |

| **Service Performed** | **Identification** | ID Number: | |
|---|---|---|---|
| ☐ Jurat | ☐ ID Card  ☐ Credible Witness | Issued By: | |
| ☐ Oath | ☐ Passport  ☐ Known Personally | | |
| ☐ Acknowledgement | ☐ Drivers License | Date Issued: | Expiration Date: |
| ☐ Other _____ | ☐ Other _____ | | |

| Document Type | Date/Time Notarized: | Document Date: | Fee Charged: |
|---|---|---|---|

| Printed Name and Address of Witness: | Phone number: |
|---|---|
| | Email: |
| | Signer's Signature: |

| Comments | Record Number |
|---|---|

# NOTARY RECORD

| Printed Name and Address of Signer: | Phone number: | Thumb Print: |
|---|---|---|
| | Email: | |
| | Signer's Signature: | |

| **Service Performed** | **Identification** | ID Number: | |
|---|---|---|---|
| ☐ Jurat | ☐ ID Card  ☐ Credible Witness | Issued By: | |
| ☐ Oath | ☐ Passport  ☐ Known Personally | | |
| ☐ Acknowledgement | ☐ Drivers License | Date Issued: | Expiration Date: |
| ☐ Other _____ | ☐ Other _____ | | |

| Document Type | Date/Time Notarized: | Document Date: | Fee Charged: |
|---|---|---|---|

| Printed Name and Address of Witness: | Phone number: |
|---|---|
| | Email: |
| | Signer's Signature: |

| Comments | Record Number |
|---|---|

# NOTARY RECORD

| Printed Name and Address of Signer: | Phone number: | Thumb Print: |
|---|---|---|
| | Email: | |
| | Signer's Signature: | |

| **Service Performed** | **Identification** | ID Number: | |
|---|---|---|---|
| ☐ Jurat | ☐ ID Card ☐ Credible Witness | Issued By: | |
| ☐ Oath | ☐ Passport ☐ Known Personally | | |
| ☐ Acknowledgement | ☐ Drivers License | Date Issued: | Expiration Date: |
| ☐ Other _____ | ☐ Other _____ | | |

| Document Type | Date/Time Notarized: | Document Date: | Fee Charged: |
|---|---|---|---|

| Printed Name and Address of Witness: | Phone number: |
|---|---|
| | Email: |
| | Signer's Signature: |

| Comments | Record Number |
|---|---|

---

# NOTARY RECORD

| Printed Name and Address of Signer: | Phone number: | Thumb Print: |
|---|---|---|
| | Email: | |
| | Signer's Signature: | |

| **Service Performed** | **Identification** | ID Number: | |
|---|---|---|---|
| ☐ Jurat | ☐ ID Card ☐ Credible Witness | Issued By: | |
| ☐ Oath | ☐ Passport ☐ Known Personally | | |
| ☐ Acknowledgement | ☐ Drivers License | Date Issued: | Expiration Date: |
| ☐ Other _____ | ☐ Other _____ | | |

| Document Type | Date/Time Notarized: | Document Date: | Fee Charged: |
|---|---|---|---|

| Printed Name and Address of Witness: | Phone number: |
|---|---|
| | Email: |
| | Signer's Signature: |

| Comments | Record Number |
|---|---|

# NOTARY RECORD

| Printed Name and Address of Signer: | Phone number: | Thumb Print: |
|---|---|---|
| | Email: | |
| | Signer's Signature: | |

| Service Performed | Identification | | ID Number: | |
|---|---|---|---|---|
| ☐ Jurat | ☐ ID Card | ☐ Credible Witness | Issued By: | |
| ☐ Oath | ☐ Passport | ☐ Known Personally | | |
| ☐ Acknowledgement | ☐ Drivers License | | Date Issued: | Expiration Date: |
| ☐ Other _____ | ☐ Other _____ | | | |

| Document Type | Date/Time Notarized: | Document Date: | Fee Charged: |
|---|---|---|---|

| Printed Name and Address of Witness: | Phone number: |
|---|---|
| | Email: |
| | Signer's Signature: |

| Comments | Record Number |
|---|---|

# NOTARY RECORD

| Printed Name and Address of Signer: | Phone number: | Thumb Print: |
|---|---|---|
| | Email: | |
| | Signer's Signature: | |

| Service Performed | Identification | | ID Number: | |
|---|---|---|---|---|
| ☐ Jurat | ☐ ID Card | ☐ Credible Witness | Issued By: | |
| ☐ Oath | ☐ Passport | ☐ Known Personally | | |
| ☐ Acknowledgement | ☐ Drivers License | | Date Issued: | Expiration Date: |
| ☐ Other _____ | ☐ Other _____ | | | |

| Document Type | Date/Time Notarized: | Document Date: | Fee Charged: |
|---|---|---|---|

| Printed Name and Address of Witness: | Phone number: |
|---|---|
| | Email: |
| | Signer's Signature: |

| Comments | Record Number |
|---|---|

# NOTARY RECORD

| Printed Name and Address of Signer: | Phone number: | Thumb Print: |
|---|---|---|
| | Email: | |
| | Signer's Signature: | |

| Service Performed | Identification | | ID Number: | |
|---|---|---|---|---|
| ☐ Jurat | ☐ ID Card | ☐ Credible Witness | Issued By: | |
| ☐ Oath | ☐ Passport | ☐ Known Personally | | |
| ☐ Acknowledgement | ☐ Drivers License | | Date Issued: | Expiration Date: |
| ☐ Other _____ | ☐ Other _____ | | | |

| Document Type | Date/Time Notarized: | Document Date: | Fee Charged: |
|---|---|---|---|

| Printed Name and Address of Witness: | Phone number: |
|---|---|
| | Email: |
| | Signer's Signature: |

| Comments | Record Number |
|---|---|

# NOTARY RECORD

| Printed Name and Address of Signer: | Phone number: | Thumb Print: |
|---|---|---|
| | Email: | |
| | Signer's Signature: | |

| Service Performed | Identification | | ID Number: | |
|---|---|---|---|---|
| ☐ Jurat | ☐ ID Card | ☐ Credible Witness | Issued By: | |
| ☐ Oath | ☐ Passport | ☐ Known Personally | | |
| ☐ Acknowledgement | ☐ Drivers License | | Date Issued: | Expiration Date: |
| ☐ Other _____ | ☐ Other _____ | | | |

| Document Type | Date/Time Notarized: | Document Date: | Fee Charged: |
|---|---|---|---|

| Printed Name and Address of Witness: | Phone number: |
|---|---|
| | Email: |
| | Signer's Signature: |

| Comments | Record Number |
|---|---|

# NOTARY RECORD

**Printed Name and Address of Signer:**

**Phone number:**

**Email:**

**Signer's Signature:**

**Thumb Print:**

| Service Performed | Identification | ID Number: | |
|---|---|---|---|
| ☐ Jurat | ☐ ID Card ☐ Credible Witness | Issued By: | |
| ☐ Oath | ☐ Passport ☐ Known Personally | | |
| ☐ Acknowledgement | ☐ Drivers License | Date Issued: | Expiration Date: |
| ☐ Other _____ | ☐ Other _____ | | |

| Document Type | Date/Time Notarized: | Document Date: | Fee Charged: |
|---|---|---|---|

**Printed Name and Address of Witness:**

**Phone number:**

**Email:**

**Signer's Signature:**

**Comments**

**Record Number**

---

# NOTARY RECORD

**Printed Name and Address of Signer:**

**Phone number:**

**Email:**

**Signer's Signature:**

**Thumb Print:**

| Service Performed | Identification | ID Number: | |
|---|---|---|---|
| ☐ Jurat | ☐ ID Card ☐ Credible Witness | Issued By: | |
| ☐ Oath | ☐ Passport ☐ Known Personally | | |
| ☐ Acknowledgement | ☐ Drivers License | Date Issued: | Expiration Date: |
| ☐ Other _____ | ☐ Other _____ | | |

| Document Type | Date/Time Notarized: | Document Date: | Fee Charged: |
|---|---|---|---|

**Printed Name and Address of Witness:**

**Phone number:**

**Email:**

**Signer's Signature:**

**Comments**

**Record Number**

# NOTARY RECORD

| Printed Name and Address of Signer: | Phone number: | Thumb Print: |
| --- | --- | --- |
| | Email: | |
| | Signer's Signature: | |

| Service Performed | Identification | | ID Number: | |
| --- | --- | --- | --- | --- |
| ☐ Jurat | ☐ ID Card | ☐ Credible Witness | Issued By: | |
| ☐ Oath | ☐ Passport | ☐ Known Personally | | |
| ☐ Acknowledgement | ☐ Drivers License | | Date Issued: | Expiration Date: |
| ☐ Other _____ | ☐ Other _____ | | | |

| Document Type | Date/Time Notarized: | Document Date: | Fee Charged: |
| --- | --- | --- | --- |

| Printed Name and Address of Witness: | Phone number: |
| --- | --- |
| | Email: |
| | Signer's Signature: |

| Comments | Record Number |
| --- | --- |

# NOTARY RECORD

| Printed Name and Address of Signer: | Phone number: | Thumb Print: |
| --- | --- | --- |
| | Email: | |
| | Signer's Signature: | |

| Service Performed | Identification | | ID Number: | |
| --- | --- | --- | --- | --- |
| ☐ Jurat | ☐ ID Card | ☐ Credible Witness | Issued By: | |
| ☐ Oath | ☐ Passport | ☐ Known Personally | | |
| ☐ Acknowledgement | ☐ Drivers License | | Date Issued: | Expiration Date: |
| ☐ Other _____ | ☐ Other _____ | | | |

| Document Type | Date/Time Notarized: | Document Date: | Fee Charged: |
| --- | --- | --- | --- |

| Printed Name and Address of Witness: | Phone number: |
| --- | --- |
| | Email: |
| | Signer's Signature: |

| Comments | Record Number |
| --- | --- |

# NOTARY RECORD

| Printed Name and Address of Signer: | Phone number: | Thumb Print: |
|---|---|---|
| | Email: | |
| | Signer's Signature: | |

| **Service Performed** | **Identification** | ID Number: | |
|---|---|---|---|
| ☐ Jurat | ☐ ID Card  ☐ Credible Witness | Issued By: | |
| ☐ Oath | ☐ Passport  ☐ Known Personally | | |
| ☐ Acknowledgement | ☐ Drivers License | Date Issued: | Expiration Date: |
| ☐ Other _____ | ☐ Other _____ | | |

| Document Type | Date/Time Notarized: | Document Date: | Fee Charged: |
|---|---|---|---|

| Printed Name and Address of Witness: | Phone number: |
|---|---|
| | Email: |
| | Signer's Signature: |

| Comments | Record Number |
|---|---|

# NOTARY RECORD

| Printed Name and Address of Signer: | Phone number: | Thumb Print: |
|---|---|---|
| | Email: | |
| | Signer's Signature: | |

| **Service Performed** | **Identification** | ID Number: | |
|---|---|---|---|
| ☐ Jurat | ☐ ID Card  ☐ Credible Witness | Issued By: | |
| ☐ Oath | ☐ Passport  ☐ Known Personally | | |
| ☐ Acknowledgement | ☐ Drivers License | Date Issued: | Expiration Date: |
| ☐ Other _____ | ☐ Other _____ | | |

| Document Type | Date/Time Notarized: | Document Date: | Fee Charged: |
|---|---|---|---|

| Printed Name and Address of Witness: | Phone number: |
|---|---|
| | Email: |
| | Signer's Signature: |

| Comments | Record Number |
|---|---|

# NOTARY RECORD

**Printed Name and Address of Signer:**

| Phone number: |
| Email: |
| Signer's Signature: |

**Thumb Print:**

| **Service Performed** | **Identification** | | ID Number: | |
|---|---|---|---|---|
| ☐ Jurat | ☐ ID Card | ☐ Credible Witness | Issued By: | |
| ☐ Oath | ☐ Passport | ☐ Known Personally | | |
| ☐ Acknowledgement | ☐ Drivers License | | Date Issued: | Expiration Date: |
| ☐ Other _____ | ☐ Other _____ | | | |

| Document Type | Date/Time Notarized: | Document Date: | Fee Charged: |
|---|---|---|---|

**Printed Name and Address of Witness:**

| Phone number: |
| Email: |
| Signer's Signature: |

| Comments | Record Number |
|---|---|

---

# NOTARY RECORD

**Printed Name and Address of Signer:**

| Phone number: |
| Email: |
| Signer's Signature: |

**Thumb Print:**

| **Service Performed** | **Identification** | | ID Number: | |
|---|---|---|---|---|
| ☐ Jurat | ☐ ID Card | ☐ Credible Witness | Issued By: | |
| ☐ Oath | ☐ Passport | ☐ Known Personally | | |
| ☐ Acknowledgement | ☐ Drivers License | | Date Issued: | Expiration Date: |
| ☐ Other _____ | ☐ Other _____ | | | |

| Document Type | Date/Time Notarized: | Document Date: | Fee Charged: |
|---|---|---|---|

**Printed Name and Address of Witness:**

| Phone number: |
| Email: |
| Signer's Signature: |

| Comments | Record Number |
|---|---|

# NOTARY RECORD

| Printed Name and Address of Signer: | Phone number: | Thumb Print: |
|---|---|---|
| | Email: | |
| | Signer's Signature: | |

| Service Performed | Identification | ID Number: | |
|---|---|---|---|
| ☐ Jurat | ☐ ID Card   ☐ Credible Witness | Issued By: | |
| ☐ Oath | ☐ Passport   ☐ Known Personally | | |
| ☐ Acknowledgement | ☐ Drivers License | Date Issued: | Expiration Date: |
| ☐ Other _____ | ☐ Other _____ | | |

| Document Type | Date/Time Notarized: | Document Date: | Fee Charged: |
|---|---|---|---|

| Printed Name and Address of Witness: | Phone number: |
|---|---|
| | Email: |
| | Signer's Signature: |

| Comments | Record Number |
|---|---|

---

# NOTARY RECORD

| Printed Name and Address of Signer: | Phone number: | Thumb Print: |
|---|---|---|
| | Email: | |
| | Signer's Signature: | |

| Service Performed | Identification | ID Number: | |
|---|---|---|---|
| ☐ Jurat | ☐ ID Card   ☐ Credible Witness | Issued By: | |
| ☐ Oath | ☐ Passport   ☐ Known Personally | | |
| ☐ Acknowledgement | ☐ Drivers License | Date Issued: | Expiration Date: |
| ☐ Other _____ | ☐ Other _____ | | |

| Document Type | Date/Time Notarized: | Document Date: | Fee Charged: |
|---|---|---|---|

| Printed Name and Address of Witness: | Phone number: |
|---|---|
| | Email: |
| | Signer's Signature: |

| Comments | Record Number |
|---|---|

# NOTARY RECORD

| Printed Name and Address of Signer: | Phone number: | Thumb Print: |
|---|---|---|
| | Email: | |
| | Signer's Signature: | |

| Service Performed | Identification | | ID Number: | |
|---|---|---|---|---|
| ☐ Jurat | ☐ ID Card | ☐ Credible Witness | Issued By: | |
| ☐ Oath | ☐ Passport | ☐ Known Personally | | |
| ☐ Acknowledgement | ☐ Drivers License | | Date Issued: | Expiration Date: |
| ☐ Other _____ | ☐ Other _____ | | | |

| Document Type | Date/Time Notarized: | Document Date: | Fee Charged: |
|---|---|---|---|

| Printed Name and Address of Witness: | Phone number: |
|---|---|
| | Email: |
| | Signer's Signature: |

| Comments | Record Number |
|---|---|

# NOTARY RECORD

| Printed Name and Address of Signer: | Phone number: | Thumb Print: |
|---|---|---|
| | Email: | |
| | Signer's Signature: | |

| Service Performed | Identification | | ID Number: | |
|---|---|---|---|---|
| ☐ Jurat | ☐ ID Card | ☐ Credible Witness | Issued By: | |
| ☐ Oath | ☐ Passport | ☐ Known Personally | | |
| ☐ Acknowledgement | ☐ Drivers License | | Date Issued: | Expiration Date: |
| ☐ Other _____ | ☐ Other _____ | | | |

| Document Type | Date/Time Notarized: | Document Date: | Fee Charged: |
|---|---|---|---|

| Printed Name and Address of Witness: | Phone number: |
|---|---|
| | Email: |
| | Signer's Signature: |

| Comments | Record Number |
|---|---|

# NOTARY RECORD

| Printed Name and Address of Signer: | Phone number: | Thumb Print: |
|---|---|---|
| | Email: | |
| | Signer's Signature: | |

| **Service Performed** | **Identification** | ID Number: | |
|---|---|---|---|
| ☐ Jurat | ☐ ID Card    ☐ Credible Witness | | |
| ☐ Oath | ☐ Passport    ☐ Known Personally | Issued By: | |
| ☐ Acknowledgement | ☐ Drivers License | | |
| ☐ Other _____ | ☐ Other _____ | Date Issued: | Expiration Date: |

| Document Type | Date/Time Notarized: | Document Date: | Fee Charged: |
|---|---|---|---|

| Printed Name and Address of Witness: | Phone number: |
|---|---|
| | Email: |
| | Signer's Signature: |

| Comments | Record Number |
|---|---|

---

# NOTARY RECORD

| Printed Name and Address of Signer: | Phone number: | Thumb Print: |
|---|---|---|
| | Email: | |
| | Signer's Signature: | |

| **Service Performed** | **Identification** | ID Number: | |
|---|---|---|---|
| ☐ Jurat | ☐ ID Card    ☐ Credible Witness | | |
| ☐ Oath | ☐ Passport    ☐ Known Personally | Issued By: | |
| ☐ Acknowledgement | ☐ Drivers License | | |
| ☐ Other _____ | ☐ Other _____ | Date Issued: | Expiration Date: |

| Document Type | Date/Time Notarized: | Document Date: | Fee Charged: |
|---|---|---|---|

| Printed Name and Address of Witness: | Phone number: |
|---|---|
| | Email: |
| | Signer's Signature: |

| Comments | Record Number |
|---|---|

# NOTARY RECORD

| Printed Name and Address of Signer: | Phone number: | Thumb Print: |
|---|---|---|
| | Email: | |
| | Signer's Signature: | |

| Service Performed | Identification | ID Number: | |
|---|---|---|---|
| ☐ Jurat | ☐ ID Card  ☐ Credible Witness | Issued By: | |
| ☐ Oath | ☐ Passport  ☐ Known Personally | | |
| ☐ Acknowledgement | ☐ Drivers License | Date Issued: | Expiration Date: |
| ☐ Other _____ | ☐ Other _____ | | |

| Document Type | Date/Time Notarized: | Document Date: | Fee Charged: |
|---|---|---|---|

| Printed Name and Address of Witness: | Phone number: |
|---|---|
| | Email: |
| | Signer's Signature: |

| Comments | Record Number |
|---|---|

---

# NOTARY RECORD

| Printed Name and Address of Signer: | Phone number: | Thumb Print: |
|---|---|---|
| | Email: | |
| | Signer's Signature: | |

| Service Performed | Identification | ID Number: | |
|---|---|---|---|
| ☐ Jurat | ☐ ID Card  ☐ Credible Witness | Issued By: | |
| ☐ Oath | ☐ Passport  ☐ Known Personally | | |
| ☐ Acknowledgement | ☐ Drivers License | Date Issued: | Expiration Date: |
| ☐ Other _____ | ☐ Other _____ | | |

| Document Type | Date/Time Notarized: | Document Date: | Fee Charged: |
|---|---|---|---|

| Printed Name and Address of Witness: | Phone number: |
|---|---|
| | Email: |
| | Signer's Signature: |

| Comments | Record Number |
|---|---|

# NOTARY RECORD

**Printed Name and Address of Signer:**

Phone number:

Email:

Signer's Signature:

Thumb Print:

| **Service Performed** | **Identification** | | |
|---|---|---|---|
| ☐ Jurat | ☐ ID Card | ☐ Credible Witness | ID Number: |
| ☐ Oath | ☐ Passport | ☐ Known Personally | Issued By: |
| ☐ Acknowledgement | ☐ Drivers License | | |
| ☐ Other _____ | ☐ Other _____ | | Date Issued: / Expiration Date: |

| Document Type | Date/Time Notarized: | Document Date: | Fee Charged: |
|---|---|---|---|

**Printed Name and Address of Witness:**

Phone number:

Email:

Signer's Signature:

| Comments | Record Number |
|---|---|

# NOTARY RECORD

**Printed Name and Address of Signer:**

Phone number:

Email:

Signer's Signature:

Thumb Print:

| **Service Performed** | **Identification** | | |
|---|---|---|---|
| ☐ Jurat | ☐ ID Card | ☐ Credible Witness | ID Number: |
| ☐ Oath | ☐ Passport | ☐ Known Personally | Issued By: |
| ☐ Acknowledgement | ☐ Drivers License | | |
| ☐ Other _____ | ☐ Other _____ | | Date Issued: / Expiration Date: |

| Document Type | Date/Time Notarized: | Document Date: | Fee Charged: |
|---|---|---|---|

**Printed Name and Address of Witness:**

Phone number:

Email:

Signer's Signature:

| Comments | Record Number |
|---|---|

# NOTARY RECORD

| Printed Name and Address of Signer: | Phone number: | Thumb Print: |
|---|---|---|
| | Email: | |
| | Signer's Signature: | |

| **Service Performed** | **Identification** | ID Number: | |
|---|---|---|---|
| ☐ Jurat | ☐ ID Card   ☐ Credible Witness | Issued By: | |
| ☐ Oath | ☐ Passport   ☐ Known Personally | | |
| ☐ Acknowledgement | ☐ Drivers License | Date Issued: | Expiration Date: |
| ☐ Other _____ | ☐ Other _____ | | |

| Document Type | Date/Time Notarized: | Document Date: | Fee Charged: |
|---|---|---|---|

| Printed Name and Address of Witness: | Phone number: |
|---|---|
| | Email: |
| | Signer's Signature: |

| Comments | Record Number |
|---|---|

---

# NOTARY RECORD

| Printed Name and Address of Signer: | Phone number: | Thumb Print: |
|---|---|---|
| | Email: | |
| | Signer's Signature: | |

| **Service Performed** | **Identification** | ID Number: | |
|---|---|---|---|
| ☐ Jurat | ☐ ID Card   ☐ Credible Witness | Issued By: | |
| ☐ Oath | ☐ Passport   ☐ Known Personally | | |
| ☐ Acknowledgement | ☐ Drivers License | Date Issued: | Expiration Date: |
| ☐ Other _____ | ☐ Other _____ | | |

| Document Type | Date/Time Notarized: | Document Date: | Fee Charged: |
|---|---|---|---|

| Printed Name and Address of Witness: | Phone number: |
|---|---|
| | Email: |
| | Signer's Signature: |

| Comments | Record Number |
|---|---|

# NOTARY RECORD

| Printed Name and Address of Signer: | Phone number: | Thumb Print: |
|---|---|---|
| | Email: | |
| | Signer's Signature: | |

| **Service Performed** | **Identification** | ID Number: | |
|---|---|---|---|
| ☐ Jurat | ☐ ID Card  ☐ Credible Witness | Issued By: | |
| ☐ Oath | ☐ Passport  ☐ Known Personally | | |
| ☐ Acknowledgement | ☐ Drivers License | Date Issued: | Expiration Date: |
| ☐ Other _____ | ☐ Other _____ | | |

| Document Type | Date/Time Notarized: | Document Date: | Fee Charged: |
|---|---|---|---|

| Printed Name and Address of Witness: | Phone number: |
|---|---|
| | Email: |
| | Signer's Signature: |

| Comments | Record Number |
|---|---|

# NOTARY RECORD

| Printed Name and Address of Signer: | Phone number: | Thumb Print: |
|---|---|---|
| | Email: | |
| | Signer's Signature: | |

| **Service Performed** | **Identification** | ID Number: | |
|---|---|---|---|
| ☐ Jurat | ☐ ID Card  ☐ Credible Witness | Issued By: | |
| ☐ Oath | ☐ Passport  ☐ Known Personally | | |
| ☐ Acknowledgement | ☐ Drivers License | Date Issued: | Expiration Date: |
| ☐ Other _____ | ☐ Other _____ | | |

| Document Type | Date/Time Notarized: | Document Date: | Fee Charged: |
|---|---|---|---|

| Printed Name and Address of Witness: | Phone number: |
|---|---|
| | Email: |
| | Signer's Signature: |

| Comments | Record Number |
|---|---|

# NOTARY RECORD

| Printed Name and Address of Signer: | Phone number: | Thumb Print: |
|---|---|---|
| | Email: | |
| | Signer's Signature: | |

| Service Performed | Identification | ID Number: | |
|---|---|---|---|
| ☐ Jurat | ☐ ID Card  ☐ Credible Witness | Issued By: | |
| ☐ Oath | ☐ Passport  ☐ Known Personally | | |
| ☐ Acknowledgement | ☐ Drivers License | Date Issued: | Expiration Date: |
| ☐ Other _____ | ☐ Other _____ | | |

| Document Type | Date/Time Notarized: | Document Date: | Fee Charged: |
|---|---|---|---|

| Printed Name and Address of Witness: | Phone number: |
|---|---|
| | Email: |
| | Signer's Signature: |

| Comments | Record Number |
|---|---|

# NOTARY RECORD

| Printed Name and Address of Signer: | Phone number: | Thumb Print: |
|---|---|---|
| | Email: | |
| | Signer's Signature: | |

| Service Performed | Identification | ID Number: | |
|---|---|---|---|
| ☐ Jurat | ☐ ID Card  ☐ Credible Witness | Issued By: | |
| ☐ Oath | ☐ Passport  ☐ Known Personally | | |
| ☐ Acknowledgement | ☐ Drivers License | Date Issued: | Expiration Date: |
| ☐ Other _____ | ☐ Other _____ | | |

| Document Type | Date/Time Notarized: | Document Date: | Fee Charged: |
|---|---|---|---|

| Printed Name and Address of Witness: | Phone number: |
|---|---|
| | Email: |
| | Signer's Signature: |

| Comments | Record Number |
|---|---|

# NOTARY RECORD

| Printed Name and Address of Signer: | Phone number: | Thumb Print: |
|---|---|---|
| | Email: | |
| | Signer's Signature: | |

| Service Performed | Identification | ID Number: | |
|---|---|---|---|
| ☐ Jurat | ☐ ID Card  ☐ Credible Witness | Issued By: | |
| ☐ Oath | ☐ Passport  ☐ Known Personally | | |
| ☐ Acknowledgement | ☐ Drivers License | Date Issued: | Expiration Date: |
| ☐ Other _____ | ☐ Other _____ | | |

| Document Type | Date/Time Notarized: | Document Date: | Fee Charged: |
|---|---|---|---|

| Printed Name and Address of Witness: | Phone number: |
|---|---|
| | Email: |
| | Signer's Signature: |

| Comments | Record Number |
|---|---|

---

# NOTARY RECORD

| Printed Name and Address of Signer: | Phone number: | Thumb Print: |
|---|---|---|
| | Email: | |
| | Signer's Signature: | |

| Service Performed | Identification | ID Number: | |
|---|---|---|---|
| ☐ Jurat | ☐ ID Card  ☐ Credible Witness | Issued By: | |
| ☐ Oath | ☐ Passport  ☐ Known Personally | | |
| ☐ Acknowledgement | ☐ Drivers License | Date Issued: | Expiration Date: |
| ☐ Other _____ | ☐ Other _____ | | |

| Document Type | Date/Time Notarized: | Document Date: | Fee Charged: |
|---|---|---|---|

| Printed Name and Address of Witness: | Phone number: |
|---|---|
| | Email: |
| | Signer's Signature: |

| Comments | Record Number |
|---|---|

# NOTARY RECORD

| Printed Name and Address of Signer: | Phone number: | Thumb Print: |
|---|---|---|
| | Email: | |
| | Signer's Signature: | |

| **Service Performed** | **Identification** | ID Number: | |
|---|---|---|---|
| ☐ Jurat | ☐ ID Card  ☐ Credible Witness | Issued By: | |
| ☐ Oath | ☐ Passport  ☐ Known Personally | | |
| ☐ Acknowledgement | ☐ Drivers License | Date Issued: | Expiration Date: |
| ☐ Other _____ | ☐ Other _____ | | |
| Document Type | Date/Time Notarized: | Document Date: | Fee Charged: |

| Printed Name and Address of Witness: | Phone number: |
|---|---|
| | Email: |
| | Signer's Signature: |

| Comments | Record Number |
|---|---|

# NOTARY RECORD

| Printed Name and Address of Signer: | Phone number: | Thumb Print: |
|---|---|---|
| | Email: | |
| | Signer's Signature: | |

| **Service Performed** | **Identification** | ID Number: | |
|---|---|---|---|
| ☐ Jurat | ☐ ID Card  ☐ Credible Witness | Issued By: | |
| ☐ Oath | ☐ Passport  ☐ Known Personally | | |
| ☐ Acknowledgement | ☐ Drivers License | Date Issued: | Expiration Date: |
| ☐ Other _____ | ☐ Other _____ | | |
| Document Type | Date/Time Notarized: | Document Date: | Fee Charged: |

| Printed Name and Address of Witness: | Phone number: |
|---|---|
| | Email: |
| | Signer's Signature: |

| Comments | Record Number |
|---|---|

# NOTARY RECORD

| Printed Name and Address of Signer: | Phone number: | Thumb Print: |
|---|---|---|
| | Email: | |
| | Signer's Signature: | |

| **Service Performed** | **Identification** | ID Number: | |
|---|---|---|---|
| ☐ Jurat | ☐ ID Card  ☐ Credible Witness | Issued By: | |
| ☐ Oath | ☐ Passport  ☐ Known Personally | | |
| ☐ Acknowledgement | ☐ Drivers License | Date Issued: | Expiration Date: |
| ☐ Other _____ | ☐ Other _____ | | |

| Document Type | Date/Time Notarized: | Document Date: | Fee Charged: |
|---|---|---|---|

| Printed Name and Address of Witness: | Phone number: |
|---|---|
| | Email: |
| | Signer's Signature: |

| Comments | Record Number |
|---|---|

# NOTARY RECORD

| Printed Name and Address of Signer: | Phone number: | Thumb Print: |
|---|---|---|
| | Email: | |
| | Signer's Signature: | |

| **Service Performed** | **Identification** | ID Number: | |
|---|---|---|---|
| ☐ Jurat | ☐ ID Card  ☐ Credible Witness | Issued By: | |
| ☐ Oath | ☐ Passport  ☐ Known Personally | | |
| ☐ Acknowledgement | ☐ Drivers License | Date Issued: | Expiration Date: |
| ☐ Other _____ | ☐ Other _____ | | |

| Document Type | Date/Time Notarized: | Document Date: | Fee Charged: |
|---|---|---|---|

| Printed Name and Address of Witness: | Phone number: |
|---|---|
| | Email: |
| | Signer's Signature: |

| Comments | Record Number |
|---|---|

# NOTARY RECORD

| Printed Name and Address of Signer: | Phone number: | Thumb Print: |
|---|---|---|
| | Email: | |
| | Signer's Signature: | |

**Service Performed**
- ☐ Jurat
- ☐ Oath
- ☐ Acknowledgement
- ☐ Other _____

**Identification**
- ☐ ID Card
- ☐ Passport
- ☐ Drivers License
- ☐ Other _____
- ☐ Credible Witness
- ☐ Known Personally

| ID Number: | |
|---|---|
| Issued By: | |
| Date Issued: | Expiration Date: |

| Document Type | Date/Time Notarized: | Document Date: | Fee Charged: |
|---|---|---|---|

| Printed Name and Address of Witness: | Phone number: |
|---|---|
| | Email: |
| | Signer's Signature: |

| Comments | Record Number |
|---|---|

---

# NOTARY RECORD

| Printed Name and Address of Signer: | Phone number: | Thumb Print: |
|---|---|---|
| | Email: | |
| | Signer's Signature: | |

**Service Performed**
- ☐ Jurat
- ☐ Oath
- ☐ Acknowledgement
- ☐ Other _____

**Identification**
- ☐ ID Card
- ☐ Passport
- ☐ Drivers License
- ☐ Other _____
- ☐ Credible Witness
- ☐ Known Personally

| ID Number: | |
|---|---|
| Issued By: | |
| Date Issued: | Expiration Date: |

| Document Type | Date/Time Notarized: | Document Date: | Fee Charged: |
|---|---|---|---|

| Printed Name and Address of Witness: | Phone number: |
|---|---|
| | Email: |
| | Signer's Signature: |

| Comments | Record Number |
|---|---|

# NOTARY RECORD

| Printed Name and Address of Signer: | Phone number: | Thumb Print: |
|---|---|---|
| | Email: | |
| | Signer's Signature: | |

| **Service Performed** | **Identification** | ID Number: | |
|---|---|---|---|
| ☐ Jurat | ☐ ID Card   ☐ Credible Witness | Issued By: | |
| ☐ Oath | ☐ Passport   ☐ Known Personally | | |
| ☐ Acknowledgement | ☐ Drivers License | Date Issued: | Expiration Date: |
| ☐ Other _____ | ☐ Other _____ | | |

| Document Type | Date/Time Notarized: | Document Date: | Fee Charged: |
|---|---|---|---|

| Printed Name and Address of Witness: | Phone number: |
|---|---|
| | Email: |
| | Signer's Signature: |

| Comments | Record Number |
|---|---|

# NOTARY RECORD

| Printed Name and Address of Signer: | Phone number: | Thumb Print: |
|---|---|---|
| | Email: | |
| | Signer's Signature: | |

| **Service Performed** | **Identification** | ID Number: | |
|---|---|---|---|
| ☐ Jurat | ☐ ID Card   ☐ Credible Witness | Issued By: | |
| ☐ Oath | ☐ Passport   ☐ Known Personally | | |
| ☐ Acknowledgement | ☐ Drivers License | Date Issued: | Expiration Date: |
| ☐ Other _____ | ☐ Other _____ | | |

| Document Type | Date/Time Notarized: | Document Date: | Fee Charged: |
|---|---|---|---|

| Printed Name and Address of Witness: | Phone number: |
|---|---|
| | Email: |
| | Signer's Signature: |

| Comments | Record Number |
|---|---|

# NOTARY RECORD

| Printed Name and Address of Signer: | Phone number: | Thumb Print: |
|---|---|---|
| | Email: | |
| | Signer's Signature: | |

| **Service Performed** | **Identification** | ID Number: | |
|---|---|---|---|
| ☐ Jurat | ☐ ID Card   ☐ Credible Witness | Issued By: | |
| ☐ Oath | ☐ Passport   ☐ Known Personally | | |
| ☐ Acknowledgement | ☐ Drivers License | Date Issued: | Expiration Date: |
| ☐ Other _____ | ☐ Other _____ | | |

| Document Type | Date/Time Notarized: | Document Date: | Fee Charged: |
|---|---|---|---|

| Printed Name and Address of Witness: | Phone number: |
|---|---|
| | Email: |
| | Signer's Signature: |

| Comments | Record Number |
|---|---|

# NOTARY RECORD

| Printed Name and Address of Signer: | Phone number: | Thumb Print: |
|---|---|---|
| | Email: | |
| | Signer's Signature: | |

| **Service Performed** | **Identification** | ID Number: | |
|---|---|---|---|
| ☐ Jurat | ☐ ID Card   ☐ Credible Witness | Issued By: | |
| ☐ Oath | ☐ Passport   ☐ Known Personally | | |
| ☐ Acknowledgement | ☐ Drivers License | Date Issued: | Expiration Date: |
| ☐ Other _____ | ☐ Other _____ | | |

| Document Type | Date/Time Notarized: | Document Date: | Fee Charged: |
|---|---|---|---|

| Printed Name and Address of Witness: | Phone number: |
|---|---|
| | Email: |
| | Signer's Signature: |

| Comments | Record Number |
|---|---|

# NOTARY RECORD

| Printed Name and Address of Signer: | Phone number: | Thumb Print: |
|---|---|---|
| | Email: | |
| | Signer's Signature: | |

| **Service Performed** | **Identification** | ID Number: | |
|---|---|---|---|
| ☐ Jurat | ☐ ID Card ☐ Credible Witness | Issued By: | |
| ☐ Oath | ☐ Passport ☐ Known Personally | | |
| ☐ Acknowledgement | ☐ Drivers License | Date Issued: | Expiration Date: |
| ☐ Other _____ | ☐ Other _____ | | |

| Document Type | Date/Time Notarized: | Document Date: | Fee Charged: |
|---|---|---|---|

| Printed Name and Address of Witness: | Phone number: |
|---|---|
| | Email: |
| | Signer's Signature: |

| Comments | Record Number |
|---|---|

# NOTARY RECORD

| Printed Name and Address of Signer: | Phone number: | Thumb Print: |
|---|---|---|
| | Email: | |
| | Signer's Signature: | |

| **Service Performed** | **Identification** | ID Number: | |
|---|---|---|---|
| ☐ Jurat | ☐ ID Card ☐ Credible Witness | Issued By: | |
| ☐ Oath | ☐ Passport ☐ Known Personally | | |
| ☐ Acknowledgement | ☐ Drivers License | Date Issued: | Expiration Date: |
| ☐ Other _____ | ☐ Other _____ | | |

| Document Type | Date/Time Notarized: | Document Date: | Fee Charged: |
|---|---|---|---|

| Printed Name and Address of Witness: | Phone number: |
|---|---|
| | Email: |
| | Signer's Signature: |

| Comments | Record Number |
|---|---|

# NOTARY RECORD

| Printed Name and Address of Signer: | Phone number: | Thumb Print: |
|---|---|---|
| | Email: | |
| | Signer's Signature: | |

| **Service Performed** | **Identification** | ID Number: | |
|---|---|---|---|
| ☐ Jurat | ☐ ID Card ☐ Credible Witness | Issued By: | |
| ☐ Oath | ☐ Passport ☐ Known Personally | | |
| ☐ Acknowledgement | ☐ Drivers License | Date Issued: | Expiration Date: |
| ☐ Other _____ | ☐ Other _____ | | |

| Document Type | Date/Time Notarized: | Document Date: | Fee Charged: |
|---|---|---|---|

| Printed Name and Address of Witness: | Phone number: |
|---|---|
| | Email: |
| | Signer's Signature: |

| Comments | Record Number |
|---|---|

---

# NOTARY RECORD

| Printed Name and Address of Signer: | Phone number: | Thumb Print: |
|---|---|---|
| | Email: | |
| | Signer's Signature: | |

| **Service Performed** | **Identification** | ID Number: | |
|---|---|---|---|
| ☐ Jurat | ☐ ID Card ☐ Credible Witness | Issued By: | |
| ☐ Oath | ☐ Passport ☐ Known Personally | | |
| ☐ Acknowledgement | ☐ Drivers License | Date Issued: | Expiration Date: |
| ☐ Other _____ | ☐ Other _____ | | |

| Document Type | Date/Time Notarized: | Document Date: | Fee Charged: |
|---|---|---|---|

| Printed Name and Address of Witness: | Phone number: |
|---|---|
| | Email: |
| | Signer's Signature: |

| Comments | Record Number |
|---|---|

# NOTARY RECORD

| Printed Name and Address of Signer: | Phone number: | Thumb Print: |
| --- | --- | --- |
| | Email: | |
| | Signer's Signature: | |

| Service Performed | Identification | ID Number: | |
| --- | --- | --- | --- |
| ☐ Jurat | ☐ ID Card  ☐ Credible Witness | Issued By: | |
| ☐ Oath | ☐ Passport  ☐ Known Personally | | |
| ☐ Acknowledgement | ☐ Drivers License | Date Issued: | Expiration Date: |
| ☐ Other _____ | ☐ Other _____ | | |

| Document Type | Date/Time Notarized: | Document Date: | Fee Charged: |
| --- | --- | --- | --- |

| Printed Name and Address of Witness: | Phone number: |
| --- | --- |
| | Email: |
| | Signer's Signature: |

| Comments | Record Number |
| --- | --- |

# NOTARY RECORD

| Printed Name and Address of Signer: | Phone number: | Thumb Print: |
| --- | --- | --- |
| | Email: | |
| | Signer's Signature: | |

| Service Performed | Identification | ID Number: | |
| --- | --- | --- | --- |
| ☐ Jurat | ☐ ID Card  ☐ Credible Witness | Issued By: | |
| ☐ Oath | ☐ Passport  ☐ Known Personally | | |
| ☐ Acknowledgement | ☐ Drivers License | Date Issued: | Expiration Date: |
| ☐ Other _____ | ☐ Other _____ | | |

| Document Type | Date/Time Notarized: | Document Date: | Fee Charged: |
| --- | --- | --- | --- |

| Printed Name and Address of Witness: | Phone number: |
| --- | --- |
| | Email: |
| | Signer's Signature: |

| Comments | Record Number |
| --- | --- |

# NOTARY RECORD

| Printed Name and Address of Signer: | Phone number: | Thumb Print: |
|---|---|---|
| | Email: | |
| | Signer's Signature: | |

| Service Performed | Identification | | ID Number: | |
|---|---|---|---|---|
| ☐ Jurat | ☐ ID Card | ☐ Credible Witness | Issued By: | |
| ☐ Oath | ☐ Passport | ☐ Known Personally | | |
| ☐ Acknowledgement | ☐ Drivers License | | Date Issued: | Expiration Date: |
| ☐ Other _____ | ☐ Other _____ | | | |

| Document Type | Date/Time Notarized: | Document Date: | Fee Charged: |
|---|---|---|---|

| Printed Name and Address of Witness: | Phone number: |
|---|---|
| | Email: |
| | Signer's Signature: |

| Comments | Record Number |
|---|---|

# NOTARY RECORD

| Printed Name and Address of Signer: | Phone number: | Thumb Print: |
|---|---|---|
| | Email: | |
| | Signer's Signature: | |

| Service Performed | Identification | | ID Number: | |
|---|---|---|---|---|
| ☐ Jurat | ☐ ID Card | ☐ Credible Witness | Issued By: | |
| ☐ Oath | ☐ Passport | ☐ Known Personally | | |
| ☐ Acknowledgement | ☐ Drivers License | | Date Issued: | Expiration Date: |
| ☐ Other _____ | ☐ Other _____ | | | |

| Document Type | Date/Time Notarized: | Document Date: | Fee Charged: |
|---|---|---|---|

| Printed Name and Address of Witness: | Phone number: |
|---|---|
| | Email: |
| | Signer's Signature: |

| Comments | Record Number |
|---|---|

# NOTARY RECORD

| Printed Name and Address of Signer: | Phone number: | Thumb Print: |
|---|---|---|
| | Email: | |
| | Signer's Signature: | |

| **Service Performed** | **Identification** | | ID Number: | |
|---|---|---|---|---|
| ☐ Jurat | ☐ ID Card | ☐ Credible Witness | | |
| ☐ Oath | ☐ Passport | ☐ Known Personally | Issued By: | |
| ☐ Acknowledgement | ☐ Drivers License | | | |
| ☐ Other _____ | ☐ Other _____ | | Date Issued: | Expiration Date: |

| Document Type | Date/Time Notarized: | Document Date: | Fee Charged: |
|---|---|---|---|

| Printed Name and Address of Witness: | Phone number: |
|---|---|
| | Email: |
| | Signer's Signature: |

| Comments | Record Number |
|---|---|

# NOTARY RECORD

| Printed Name and Address of Signer: | Phone number: | Thumb Print: |
|---|---|---|
| | Email: | |
| | Signer's Signature: | |

| **Service Performed** | **Identification** | | ID Number: | |
|---|---|---|---|---|
| ☐ Jurat | ☐ ID Card | ☐ Credible Witness | | |
| ☐ Oath | ☐ Passport | ☐ Known Personally | Issued By: | |
| ☐ Acknowledgement | ☐ Drivers License | | | |
| ☐ Other _____ | ☐ Other _____ | | Date Issued: | Expiration Date: |

| Document Type | Date/Time Notarized: | Document Date: | Fee Charged: |
|---|---|---|---|

| Printed Name and Address of Witness: | Phone number: |
|---|---|
| | Email: |
| | Signer's Signature: |

| Comments | Record Number |
|---|---|

# NOTARY RECORD

| Printed Name and Address of Signer: | Phone number: | Thumb Print: |
|---|---|---|
| | Email: | |
| | Signer's Signature: | |

| Service Performed | Identification | ID Number: | |
|---|---|---|---|
| ☐ Jurat | ☐ ID Card  ☐ Credible Witness | Issued By: | |
| ☐ Oath | ☐ Passport  ☐ Known Personally | | |
| ☐ Acknowledgement | ☐ Drivers License | Date Issued: | Expiration Date: |
| ☐ Other _____ | ☐ Other _____ | | |

| Document Type | Date/Time Notarized: | Document Date: | Fee Charged: |
|---|---|---|---|

| Printed Name and Address of Witness: | Phone number: |
|---|---|
| | Email: |
| | Signer's Signature: |

| Comments | Record Number |
|---|---|

---

# NOTARY RECORD

| Printed Name and Address of Signer: | Phone number: | Thumb Print: |
|---|---|---|
| | Email: | |
| | Signer's Signature: | |

| Service Performed | Identification | ID Number: | |
|---|---|---|---|
| ☐ Jurat | ☐ ID Card  ☐ Credible Witness | Issued By: | |
| ☐ Oath | ☐ Passport  ☐ Known Personally | | |
| ☐ Acknowledgement | ☐ Drivers License | Date Issued: | Expiration Date: |
| ☐ Other _____ | ☐ Other _____ | | |

| Document Type | Date/Time Notarized: | Document Date: | Fee Charged: |
|---|---|---|---|

| Printed Name and Address of Witness: | Phone number: |
|---|---|
| | Email: |
| | Signer's Signature: |

| Comments | Record Number |
|---|---|

# NOTARY RECORD

| Printed Name and Address of Signer: | Phone number: | Thumb Print: |
|---|---|---|
| | Email: | |
| | Signer's Signature: | |

| **Service Performed** | **Identification** | | ID Number: | |
|---|---|---|---|---|
| ☐ Jurat | ☐ ID Card | ☐ Credible Witness | Issued By: | |
| ☐ Oath | ☐ Passport | ☐ Known Personally | | |
| ☐ Acknowledgement | ☐ Drivers License | | Date Issued: | Expiration Date: |
| ☐ Other _____ | ☐ Other _____ | | | |

| Document Type | Date/Time Notarized: | Document Date: | Fee Charged: |
|---|---|---|---|

| Printed Name and Address of Witness: | Phone number: |
|---|---|
| | Email: |
| | Signer's Signature: |

| Comments | Record Number |
|---|---|

# NOTARY RECORD

| Printed Name and Address of Signer: | Phone number: | Thumb Print: |
|---|---|---|
| | Email: | |
| | Signer's Signature: | |

| **Service Performed** | **Identification** | | ID Number: | |
|---|---|---|---|---|
| ☐ Jurat | ☐ ID Card | ☐ Credible Witness | Issued By: | |
| ☐ Oath | ☐ Passport | ☐ Known Personally | | |
| ☐ Acknowledgement | ☐ Drivers License | | Date Issued: | Expiration Date: |
| ☐ Other _____ | ☐ Other _____ | | | |

| Document Type | Date/Time Notarized: | Document Date: | Fee Charged: |
|---|---|---|---|

| Printed Name and Address of Witness: | Phone number: |
|---|---|
| | Email: |
| | Signer's Signature: |

| Comments | Record Number |
|---|---|

# NOTARY RECORD

| Printed Name and Address of Signer: | Phone number: | Thumb Print: |
|---|---|---|
| | Email: | |
| | Signer's Signature: | |

**Service Performed**

- ☐ Jurat
- ☐ Oath
- ☐ Acknowledgement
- ☐ Other _____

**Identification**

- ☐ ID Card
- ☐ Passport
- ☐ Drivers License
- ☐ Other _____
- ☐ Credible Witness
- ☐ Known Personally

| ID Number: | |
|---|---|
| Issued By: | |
| Date Issued: | Expiration Date: |

| Document Type | Date/Time Notarized: | Document Date: | Fee Charged: |
|---|---|---|---|

| Printed Name and Address of Witness: | Phone number: |
|---|---|
| | Email: |
| | Signer's Signature: |

| Comments | Record Number |
|---|---|

# NOTARY RECORD

| Printed Name and Address of Signer: | Phone number: | Thumb Print: |
|---|---|---|
| | Email: | |
| | Signer's Signature: | |

**Service Performed**

- ☐ Jurat
- ☐ Oath
- ☐ Acknowledgement
- ☐ Other _____

**Identification**

- ☐ ID Card
- ☐ Passport
- ☐ Drivers License
- ☐ Other _____
- ☐ Credible Witness
- ☐ Known Personally

| ID Number: | |
|---|---|
| Issued By: | |
| Date Issued: | Expiration Date: |

| Document Type | Date/Time Notarized: | Document Date: | Fee Charged: |
|---|---|---|---|

| Printed Name and Address of Witness: | Phone number: |
|---|---|
| | Email: |
| | Signer's Signature: |

| Comments | Record Number |
|---|---|

# NOTARY RECORD

| Printed Name and Address of Signer: | Phone number: | Thumb Print: |
|---|---|---|
| | Email: | |
| | Signer's Signature: | |

| Service Performed | Identification | | ID Number: | |
|---|---|---|---|---|
| ☐ Jurat | ☐ ID Card | ☐ Credible Witness | Issued By: | |
| ☐ Oath | ☐ Passport | ☐ Known Personally | | |
| ☐ Acknowledgement | ☐ Drivers License | | Date Issued: | Expiration Date: |
| ☐ Other _____ | ☐ Other _____ | | | |

| Document Type | Date/Time Notarized: | Document Date: | Fee Charged: |
|---|---|---|---|

| Printed Name and Address of Witness: | Phone number: |
|---|---|
| | Email: |
| | Signer's Signature: |

| Comments | Record Number |
|---|---|

# NOTARY RECORD

| Printed Name and Address of Signer: | Phone number: | Thumb Print: |
|---|---|---|
| | Email: | |
| | Signer's Signature: | |

| Service Performed | Identification | | ID Number: | |
|---|---|---|---|---|
| ☐ Jurat | ☐ ID Card | ☐ Credible Witness | Issued By: | |
| ☐ Oath | ☐ Passport | ☐ Known Personally | | |
| ☐ Acknowledgement | ☐ Drivers License | | Date Issued: | Expiration Date: |
| ☐ Other _____ | ☐ Other _____ | | | |

| Document Type | Date/Time Notarized: | Document Date: | Fee Charged: |
|---|---|---|---|

| Printed Name and Address of Witness: | Phone number: |
|---|---|
| | Email: |
| | Signer's Signature: |

| Comments | Record Number |
|---|---|

# NOTARY RECORD

| Printed Name and Address of Signer: | Phone number: | Thumb Print: |
|---|---|---|
| | Email: | |
| | Signer's Signature: | |

| Service Performed | Identification | | ID Number: | |
|---|---|---|---|---|
| ☐ Jurat | ☐ ID Card | ☐ Credible Witness | Issued By: | |
| ☐ Oath | ☐ Passport | ☐ Known Personally | | |
| ☐ Acknowledgement | ☐ Drivers License | | Date Issued: | Expiration Date: |
| ☐ Other _____ | ☐ Other _____ | | | |

| Document Type | Date/Time Notarized: | Document Date: | Fee Charged: |
|---|---|---|---|

| Printed Name and Address of Witness: | Phone number: |
|---|---|
| | Email: |
| | Signer's Signature: |

| Comments | Record Number |
|---|---|

# NOTARY RECORD

| Printed Name and Address of Signer: | Phone number: | Thumb Print: |
|---|---|---|
| | Email: | |
| | Signer's Signature: | |

| Service Performed | Identification | | ID Number: | |
|---|---|---|---|---|
| ☐ Jurat | ☐ ID Card | ☐ Credible Witness | Issued By: | |
| ☐ Oath | ☐ Passport | ☐ Known Personally | | |
| ☐ Acknowledgement | ☐ Drivers License | | Date Issued: | Expiration Date: |
| ☐ Other _____ | ☐ Other _____ | | | |

| Document Type | Date/Time Notarized: | Document Date: | Fee Charged: |
|---|---|---|---|

| Printed Name and Address of Witness: | Phone number: |
|---|---|
| | Email: |
| | Signer's Signature: |

| Comments | Record Number |
|---|---|

# NOTARY RECORD

| Printed Name and Address of Signer: | Phone number: | Thumb Print: |
|---|---|---|
| | Email: | |
| | Signer's Signature: | |

| **Service Performed** | **Identification** | ID Number: | |
|---|---|---|---|
| ☐ Jurat | ☐ ID Card    ☐ Credible Witness | Issued By: | |
| ☐ Oath | ☐ Passport    ☐ Known Personally | | |
| ☐ Acknowledgement | ☐ Drivers License | Date Issued: | Expiration Date: |
| ☐ Other _____ | ☐ Other _____ | | |

| Document Type | Date/Time Notarized: | Document Date: | Fee Charged: |
|---|---|---|---|

| Printed Name and Address of Witness: | Phone number: |
|---|---|
| | Email: |
| | Signer's Signature: |

| Comments | Record Number |
|---|---|

# NOTARY RECORD

| Printed Name and Address of Signer: | Phone number: | Thumb Print: |
|---|---|---|
| | Email: | |
| | Signer's Signature: | |

| **Service Performed** | **Identification** | ID Number: | |
|---|---|---|---|
| ☐ Jurat | ☐ ID Card    ☐ Credible Witness | Issued By: | |
| ☐ Oath | ☐ Passport    ☐ Known Personally | | |
| ☐ Acknowledgement | ☐ Drivers License | Date Issued: | Expiration Date: |
| ☐ Other _____ | ☐ Other _____ | | |

| Document Type | Date/Time Notarized: | Document Date: | Fee Charged: |
|---|---|---|---|

| Printed Name and Address of Witness: | Phone number: |
|---|---|
| | Email: |
| | Signer's Signature: |

| Comments | Record Number |
|---|---|

# NOTARY RECORD

| Printed Name and Address of Signer: | Phone number: | Thumb Print: |
|---|---|---|
| | Email: | |
| | Signer's Signature: | |

| Service Performed | Identification | | ID Number: | |
|---|---|---|---|---|
| ☐ Jurat | ☐ ID Card | ☐ Credible Witness | Issued By: | |
| ☐ Oath | ☐ Passport | ☐ Known Personally | | |
| ☐ Acknowledgement | ☐ Drivers License | | Date Issued: | Expiration Date: |
| ☐ Other _____ | ☐ Other _____ | | | |

| Document Type | Date/Time Notarized: | Document Date: | Fee Charged: |
|---|---|---|---|

| Printed Name and Address of Witness: | Phone number: |
|---|---|
| | Email: |
| | Signer's Signature: |

| Comments | Record Number |
|---|---|

---

# NOTARY RECORD

| Printed Name and Address of Signer: | Phone number: | Thumb Print: |
|---|---|---|
| | Email: | |
| | Signer's Signature: | |

| Service Performed | Identification | | ID Number: | |
|---|---|---|---|---|
| ☐ Jurat | ☐ ID Card | ☐ Credible Witness | Issued By: | |
| ☐ Oath | ☐ Passport | ☐ Known Personally | | |
| ☐ Acknowledgement | ☐ Drivers License | | Date Issued: | Expiration Date: |
| ☐ Other _____ | ☐ Other _____ | | | |

| Document Type | Date/Time Notarized: | Document Date: | Fee Charged: |
|---|---|---|---|

| Printed Name and Address of Witness: | Phone number: |
|---|---|
| | Email: |
| | Signer's Signature: |

| Comments | Record Number |
|---|---|

# NOTARY RECORD

| Printed Name and Address of Signer: | Phone number: | Thumb Print: |
|---|---|---|
| | Email: | |
| | Signer's Signature: | |

| **Service Performed** | **Identification** | ID Number: | |
|---|---|---|---|
| ☐ Jurat | ☐ ID Card    ☐ Credible Witness | Issued By: | |
| ☐ Oath | ☐ Passport    ☐ Known Personally | | |
| ☐ Acknowledgement | ☐ Drivers License | Date Issued: | Expiration Date: |
| ☐ Other _____ | ☐ Other _____ | | |

| Document Type | Date/Time Notarized: | Document Date: | Fee Charged: |
|---|---|---|---|

| Printed Name and Address of Witness: | Phone number: |
|---|---|
| | Email: |
| | Signer's Signature: |

| Comments | Record Number |
|---|---|

# NOTARY RECORD

| Printed Name and Address of Signer: | Phone number: | Thumb Print: |
|---|---|---|
| | Email: | |
| | Signer's Signature: | |

| **Service Performed** | **Identification** | ID Number: | |
|---|---|---|---|
| ☐ Jurat | ☐ ID Card    ☐ Credible Witness | Issued By: | |
| ☐ Oath | ☐ Passport    ☐ Known Personally | | |
| ☐ Acknowledgement | ☐ Drivers License | Date Issued: | Expiration Date: |
| ☐ Other _____ | ☐ Other _____ | | |

| Document Type | Date/Time Notarized: | Document Date: | Fee Charged: |
|---|---|---|---|

| Printed Name and Address of Witness: | Phone number: |
|---|---|
| | Email: |
| | Signer's Signature: |

| Comments | Record Number |
|---|---|